Penguin Education X3
Library of Technology
General Editor: F. W. Kellaway
Principal, Letchworth College of Technology

Fundamentals of engineering science and mathematics
Volume one
K. J. Dean

Kenneth John Dean, who holds two physics degrees, is a
Fellow of the Institution of Electrical Engineers and a corporate
member of both the Institute of Physics and the Physical Society
and the Institution of Electronic and Radio Engineers.
At present Head of the Department of Science and Electrical
Engineering at Letchworth College of Technology, he is the
author of a number of books dealing with electronics and
the principles of physics. In addition he has a full technological
certificate of the City and Guilds of London Institute, a
qualification of the type sought by students reading this book.

Fundamentals of engineering science and mathematics
Volume one

K. J. Dean

B.Sc., C.Eng., F.Inst.P., F.I.E.E., M.I.E.R.E.
Head of the Department of Science and Electrical Engineering
at Letchworth College of Technology

Penguin Books

Penguin Books Ltd, Harmondsworth,
Middlesex, England
Penguin Books Inc., 3300 Clipper Mill Road,
Baltimore, Md 21211, U.S.A.
Penguin Books Australia Ltd, Ringwood,
Victoria, Australia

First published by Penguin Books Ltd, 1967
Copyright © K. J. Dean, 1967

Made and printed in Great Britain by
Gilmour & Dean Ltd, Hamilton
Set in Monotype Times

Contents

Preface

This book is the first of two which are intended to cover the fundamentals of engineering science and mathematics. Very little mathematical ability is assumed and it is not expected that the reader will have studied science in any depth before tackling this book. However, even if he has followed a school course with some success, it is to be hoped that he will find much that is new here. An attempt has been made to present the mathematical and scientific knowledge essential to a technician in a form which is adult in approach and makes demands on observation and experiment. There is thus no acceptance of half-truths and the reader is, for instance, given some account of the atomic nature of matter and atomic structure, including some discussion of electronic shells.

The techniques of scientific observation and of multiple measurements and the estimation of errors are discussed since it is the author's opinion that these are essential requirements of any worthwhile course in science. Care has also been taken to see that these books are in line with the stated policy of the British government regarding the use of metric units; S.I. units (i.e. M.K.S. units) have therefore been stressed wherever possible, although the Celsius (centigrade) scale has been used for temperature measurements in the interests of simplicity.

The impetus to write these books came from the needs of students for the Mechanical Technicians' course (293) of the City and Guilds of London Institute, and their contents are based on the syllabus for that course, although as already explained certain additional matter has been included to help students understand the reasons for some observed phenomena. It is expected that these books will appeal to a wide group, both in schools and at colleges of further education. A direct approach to the reader has been used since it is only when the student understands the relevance of what he reads that active learning can take place.

Practical work and problems are introduced in the text and it is very desirable that these should be attempted as they occur in order to obtain the best results from these books, since subsequent work frequently depends on the results of previous experimental observations; all the experiments can be performed with simple apparatus.

A number of items which have been included are intended partly as revision to ensure that these topics are fresh in the candidate's mind, and partly as an insurance, since they will constitute a foundation for subsequent work. It is the author's opinion that if this volume started off with a catalogue of such items it would make dull reading and might in fact actively discourage the reader at a time when his whole interest and attention need to be fostered. For this reason a number of the more simple topics have been collected at the end of the book in an appendix. The reader is encouraged to look briefly at this and if its subject matter is familiar to proceed at once to chapter 1. The appendix also contains some simple formulae which he might require later on.

Whilst understanding this book does not depend on other reading, a good library and the encouragement of an experienced teacher are always desirable.

K. J. Dean
April 1967

Chapter 1
The fundamentals of calculation

We live in a time when a great deal of land is being used for new building. We have all, probably, seen open spaces where people have been at work felling trees and clearing rubble. In time, piles of bricks have appeared and foundations have been dug; later bricklayers, plasterers, joiners and painters have been busy. Now as we pass we see a house, and we know a little of the effort that had to take place before it was of any use to live in.

Houses are in great demand today of course, although we may ask what all this has to do with us. But engineers, scientists and technicians are in great demand too. The care that goes into the building of a house is the sort of care that you need to take to turn yourself into a valuable person: valuable, that is, to an employer. This is a challenge, for you only have one life, one house to build, and one chance to succeed. There is the dead wood of idleness to be cleared away before the bricks of mathematics and science can be laid. This book can show you how to lay those bricks until you have a skill to be proud of, but it cannot lay them for you.

The foundations must be prepared carefully, or cracks will later appear in your knowledge, and you will be unsure and in doubt. One of the most important foundations is the ability to calculate quickly and accurately. My part in this is to show which foundations to lay. It is foolish to waste time with unnecessary mathematics, but even worse to be uncertain of what you do know.

Accuracy

Of course we all have to be accurate, but how accurate? I read in the daily paper that the assets of a large company are 20 million pounds. Does it matter if that figure is out by 17s. 6d? Is the statement in the paper still reasonably accurate if it differs from the actual amount by a hundred pounds? .... a thousand pounds? .... a million pounds? Perhaps it depends on who wants to know. What is sufficiently accurate for a man casually reading his paper at breakfast will not be accurate enough for the man who checks the firm's books or for the tax inspector. The accuracy which is satisfactory depends on the circumstances.

Look at this statement:

$$100 \div 2 = 50$$

This is completely accurate. 100 divided by 2 is exactly 50, neither more nor less. But 100 divided by 7 may be stated as 14 or as 14·2857143 and neither is exactly correct, as you may check for yourself. Sometimes in our work there will be exact answers, but often you will have to ask yourself 'How accurately need the answer be given?' If you were dividing 100 small coins amongst 7 people, you would probably be content to give 14 to each of them, but in the work we shall meet something more than this may be required.

Two things are important here. First, the circumstances of the question will often help you to give the sort of accuracy which is required (the distance between Washington and Moscow will require quite different degrees of accuracy for the tourist and the missile designer). Second, you should be able to discover for yourself how accurate your answer is.

Examine these two statements:

(a) $100 \div 7 = 14·2$

(b) $100 \div 7 = 14·3$

Which is more accurate? It is clear that the correct answer lies somewhere between these two values. Also they only differ by 0·1 so that the greatest error which can exist here is 0·1 of a part in 14·2 or 1 part in 142. This is about 7 parts in 1000. For example, if a piece of precision metalwork had to be 142 cm. long the error might be too great were it $\frac{1}{10}$ cm. under or oversize. However, it has been stated that

$$100 \div 7 = 14·2857143$$

From this we can see that the statement (b) is more accurate than (a), for the correct result is nearer to 14·3 than to 14·2. In fact it is greater than

14·28, so that 14·3 is in error by less than 0·02 of a part in 14 parts, that is, by less than 1 part in 700 parts.

Because the accurate result was greater than 14·25 it was rounded off to 14·3. Had it been less than this, it would have been better to write 14·2. When the number ends in a 5 it is customary to round off the previous number to a higher rather than a lower one; thus 14·285 becomes 14·29, not 14·28.

When the solution is given as 14 it is said to be correct to two significant figures. 14·29 is correct to four significant figures. A significant figure is one which matters. Here '1' is the most significant figure, for it matters most, the '4' matters next, the '2' next, and '9' is the least significant. Thus, in the last paragraph, it would have been preferable to say 'When the least significant figure in a number is 5, it is usual to round off to a higher rather than a lower number'.

Earlier in this chapter, the figure of 20 million pounds was mentioned. How many significant figures are there in that? If you say '8' then you will be taken to mean that £20,000,000 is correct to the nearest £0·5. Perhaps there are only two significant figures. Then 20 million pounds is correct to within a half a million pounds. If you say there is only one significant figure then you will be within 5 million pounds of the correct sum.

It is not necessarily the case that the least significant figure is the one next to the decimal point, nor need it be the unit in which the quantity is being measured. In this example, that unit was the pound. The value of the quantity was indicated by the word 'million' and the significance of that quantity by the numbers in front of it.

Checks

A great deal of time and effort are wasted (and, incidentally, marks lost in examinations) by people who believe that their mental or written arithmetic is so good that they never make mistakes. We all make mistakes, but only the sensible people take time to check their work. Even computers, carrying out many calculations each second, are arranged to check their results.

Consider this problem, but do not attempt to calculate the exact result:

$$\frac{15\cdot95}{7\cdot994} \times \frac{14\cdot68}{0\cdot48} =$$

What sort of result do you expect to get for this problem? 6000? 0·6? A simple check will show that we may approximately write:

$$\frac{16}{8} \times \frac{14\cdot5}{0\cdot5}$$
$$= 2 \times 29$$
$$= 58$$

Thus we can guard against errors like those above. If the figures are correct, and from our check it seems likely that they are, then the answer must be about 60. Actually it is 61·021.

Can you suggest another method by which the result could be checked?

Problems 1.1

The following problems are given together with the results obtained by a student. Without attempting to solve them accurately, which of them would you say were definitely incorrect?

(1) $57\cdot2 \times 2\cdot794 \quad = \quad 15\cdot982$

(2) $86\cdot1 \div 23\cdot9 \quad = \quad 3\cdot6025$

(3) $0\cdot542 \times 0\cdot289 \quad = \quad 0\cdot1566$

(4) $0\cdot0712 \times 712 \quad = \quad 50\cdot694$

(5) $\dfrac{674 \times 121}{3892} \quad = \quad 40\cdot954$

(6) $\dfrac{0\cdot69 \times 2\cdot14}{0\cdot02} \quad = \quad 73\cdot83$

(7) $\dfrac{0\cdot004}{0\cdot018} \quad = \quad 0\cdot2222$

(8) $\dfrac{1\cdot264 \times 0\cdot89}{0\cdot26} \quad = \quad 0\cdot04327$

(9) $129\cdot2 \times 68\cdot7 \quad = \quad 8876\cdot04$

(10) $269\cdot4 \times 8\cdot1 \quad = \quad 2082\cdot14$

Look again at (10). A suitable check is as follows:

$$270 \times 8 = 2160$$

At first sight it would seem that 2082·14 is correct. It is of the correct *order of magnitude*, that is, it has four figures to the left of the decimal point and the most significant figure is the same in each case; but it is not, in fact, correct. These checks can be used to find errors of magnitude and some calculation errors, as in (5), when they occur in the most significant figure, but errors in the next figure (as here) can easily be over-looked. It should be noticed that the check can easily have a high degree of accuracy. 270 was written for 269·4. This was higher than the correct figure. 8 was written for 8·1. This was lower. Hence, when multiplying, the errors of approximation tend to cancel. The approximate result, 2160, has the two most significant figures correct. The correct result is 2182·14.

If possible, when dividing as in (2) the numbers should be rounded off so that either they are both slightly high or they are both low.

Thus, either $\dfrac{88}{24} = \dfrac{11}{3} = 3.67$

or $\dfrac{84}{23} = 3\dfrac{15}{23} = 3.65$

Common factors

Sometimes routine division can be made easier if it is noticed that there are common factors in the upper part of the fraction, or numerator, and in the lower part, or denominator. Thus in the approximation $\frac{88}{24}$ the common factor, 8, can be divided out. Nevertheless common factors have much wider use than in checking your arithmetic.

The following problems should give you some practice at noticing common factors and so simplifying your accurate calculations.

Problems 1.2

Solve the following problems, giving your answers correct to four significant figures:

(1) $\dfrac{0.72 \times 1.7 \times 4}{0.204}$

(2) $\dfrac{15.4 \times 2.7}{9 \times 0.11}$

(3) $\dfrac{0.51 \times 20}{0.07 \times 3.4}$

(4) $\dfrac{13.39 \times 0.42}{0.103}$

(5) $\dfrac{10.5 \times 6.45}{0.3 \times 7.0}$

Averages

Now suppose that these five calculations were the result of the work of a student in a science laboratory. The figures were obtained as measurements which were made in an experiment. Assume also that there is good reason to believe that the results of each calculation should be approximately the same: that is, some constant value. What is that value? If you have worked through problems 1.2 you will know that the results are all of the same order of magnitude; but which of them is the correct result?

One simple method in a case of this sort is to obtain the average of the results. Since there are *five* readings, the results of the calculations are added and divided by *five*. This is the average result. What is it in this case?[1]

If you examine your average answer, you will always find that it lies within the range of the results. That is, it is less than the highest of them (42·86) and greater than the lowest (24·00). Now consider this example:

Find the average of the following readings: 1·642, 2·396, 1·716, 1·541, 2·062, 1·869.

The sum of these readings = 11·226. This must be divided by six, since here there are six readings. Therefore the average is 1·871. Now compare each of the readings with the average reading.

$$
\begin{array}{llll}
1\cdot642 & \text{is low} & \text{by} & 0\cdot229 \\
1\cdot716 & \text{is low} & \text{by} & 0\cdot155 \\
1\cdot541 & \text{is low} & \text{by} & 0\cdot330 \\
1\cdot869 & \text{is low} & \text{by} & \underline{0\cdot002} \\
& \text{total} & & \underline{0\cdot716} \\
2\cdot396 & \text{is high by} & & \underline{0\cdot525} \\
2\cdot062 & \text{is high by} & & \underline{0\cdot191} \\
& \text{total} & & \underline{0\cdot716}
\end{array}
$$

Thus, the four low readings are exactly balanced by the two high readings. When we find the average of some results we are finding this balance. If we limit ourselves to these four significant figures we may not find it exactly, but we can get very close to the average.

For example, if we take the average of the first four readings, it is 1·82375. Then if we take this to be 1·824 to four significant figures, the total of the high readings (0·572) is not quite equal to the total of the low readings (0·573) because of this approximation.

[1]Answer on page 27.

Percentages

You may, perhaps, have asked yourself whether all these readings are equally reliable. You were told that they should all have been equal values. It is easy to understand that all sorts of outside factors may have affected the measurements which were made by the man in this practical experiment. The position of his eye in reading the scale, the accuracy of the scale itself, and any uncertainty in judging a reading which fell between two marks on the scale, may all have caused small differences in a very simple measurement. But how small should these differences be? In addition to this, the man may make a definite *error* of reading, perhaps reading 0·3 for 0·8 or something of this sort. Should this reading be excluded from the average? Also, how can such readings be detected?

In the example we have been considering, one error is very much larger than any of the others. The result, 2·396, was higher than the average by 0·525. If we temporarily exclude this reading and take the average of the others, we find that this is 1·766 and the sum of the differences between the average and either the high or the low readings is 0·399, which is almost half of the previous figure. Of course, we could go on doing this until, with only one reading left, there were no differences remaining which we could examine. How far ought this process to be taken?

To help answer this question, perhaps we should first inquire how much more reliable the new average of 1·766 is than the first one we obtained, of 1·871? Clearly the new average is lower, as we should expect it to be, since a high result (2·396) has been excluded.

One way of assessing the extent to which a reading differs from the average is to calculate the *percentage* by which it differs. To calculate this percentage, we must estimate the number of parts by which the reading differs, in this case from the average, for every one hundred parts of the average reading. For example, if in some experiment we obtain three readings:

180,   195,   225

then the average of these is 200. The difference between the lowest reading and the average is 20. The corresponding percentage error can now be found, since if this result differs from the average by 20 parts in 200 it will also differ by 10 parts in 100. It is said to be *10 per cent low*. The second reading is 5 parts low in 200, that is 2·5 per cent low. Similarly, the final reading is 12·5 per cent high. Again we find that the sum of the (percentage) differences which are lower than the average is equal to the sum of those which are higher. What then is the advantage of putting our results in the form of percentages?

Look again at the earlier example, which is repeated here but with the percentage by which each reading differs from the average. Note that a minus sign has been used to show low readings and a plus sign for high ones.

reading	difference from average	percentage difference from average
1·642	−0·229	−12·24
2·396	+0·525	+28·06
1·716	−0·155	− 8·28
1·541	−0·330	−17·64
2·062	+0·191	+10·21
1·869	−0·002	− 0·11

To find these percentage differences each result was divided by the average, thereby determining the number of parts by which it differed from the average for each part of it, and then multiplied by 100 to find the number of parts in every hundred by which it differed.

Thus, $\dfrac{0\cdot229}{1\cdot871} \times 100 = 12\cdot24$ correct to four significant figures.

It is now possible to see what a poor set of results these are, for even excluding the result which is 28 per cent high we are still left with three results which differ from the average by over 10 per cent. If our average is to be of good accuracy the results must be closer than this. We must also ask ourselves whether it is satisfactory to accept only two or three readings and take an average of them.

So far we have come to the conclusion that if an average is obtained by the process just outlined it is possible that it will itself be considerably in error. It is, therefore, often wrong to reject readings just because they differ widely from this 'average'. This argument is most likely to be true when only a small number of results are obtained. We must, therefore, always remember that when any scientific conclusion we reach is based on only a few results it can be very wide of the truth. Instead, it is always wise to obtain as many results as we reasonably can. The average which can then be obtained is more reliable than in the previous case. Whilst obvious errors can always be excluded, it is an important scientific principle to base any conclusions we reach on an adequate number of results.

Problems 1.3

1. There is good reason to believe that, except for experimental error, the following readings of the height of a column of liquid in a manometer should all be of the same value. Find the average of (a) the first 5, (b) the first 10, and (c) of all of them. Also find the maximum percentage error which any reading in each of the chosen groups has from the average for that group.

> 12·54, 14·56, 15·27, 13·69, 16·01
> 17·21, 15·30, 14·80, 14·28, 17·54
> 16·72, 16·48, 15·88, 14·96, 15·18
> 14·41, 13·56, 13·42, 12·61, 15·68

2. In question 1, how many of the readings lie within (a) 5 per cent, and (b) 10 per cent of 15·00? Express your answers as percentages of the total number of readings.

Distribution of errors

From question 1.3.2 it can be seen that many of the readings lie close to the average result, and the great majority of them are within 10 per cent of it. This is typical of the way in which the results of this kind of experiment are normally distributed about the average value. In the earlier example which was closely examined, this was not so. It is often worth while examining the results of an experiment to discover whether this 'normal distribution' has been obtained. If it has not, it will often be necessary to take further readings.

In studying this chapter you will have realized that science is very much concerned with measurements, and by taking large numbers of these it is possible to reduce considerably the experimental error which would probably exist if only a few results were obtained. It should not be thought, however, that every set of experimental results is like those we have looked at here, in which all the results are approximately of the same size. Other types of results will be examined in later chapters.

Proportions and ratios

One of the ways in which mathematics may help us in science and technology is in mechanical construction. It is not always practicable to make drawings exactly the same size as the objects they represent. Furthermore, a drawing is only a flat representation of a solid object, and the practice of technical drawing is intended to overcome this limitation. Nevertheless it is still often necessary to use scale drawings, and the engineer therefore requires to examine drawings in which all the dimensions have been scaled in some given proportion. A discussion of the way in which such drawings are prepared is of primary concern in the study of technical drawing. In the matters with which this book is concerned two questions will arise. The first is one of accuracy.

If a drawing of a flat piece of metal has been reduced from the size of the original piece, in a proportion of 10:1, what effect does this have on the accuracy with which we can read its length using a scale? What effect does it have on our ability to calculate its area? In science we must always be asking questions like these, so that we shall be able to decide the value of the things which we think we know. If a ruler is used to measure a length on the original piece of metal, we shall only be able to read the length on the drawing to an accuracy that depends on the fineness with which its scale is divided, limited by the quality of our eyesight for detail or by reliance on some optical aid. Hence the proportion to which a drawing is reduced or enlarged must depend, in part at least, on the ease with which measurements can be taken from it with the necessary degree of accuracy.

The second question which you might ask is how the area of the piece of metal compares with the area of the scale drawing of it. If its length and its width have each been reduced in a proportion of perhaps 10, then its area will have been reduced in proportion to the product of its length and width, that is 100 times.

If a scale model is made of the piece of metal, how will the volume of metal in the original compare with that of the model?[1]

These ideas of scale and proportion do not apply only to drawings and models: such things are merely examples of particular uses of the idea of proportion. If we draw a graph showing how a patient's temperature changes during his illness we are using the axes of the graph in proportion to the quantities they represent, but the quantities we are comparing are different. Can we really compare the length of the graph with the length of his illness? These are different quantities (distance and time) and perhaps one square of the graph paper represents one hour of the day, or for the other axis, ten squares represent one centigrade degree change of temperature.

Sometimes, instead of changing the scale in proportion to a fixed number, a ratio is used. In this example, for instance, four squares of the graph paper might now represent five hours. Previously, one square

[1]Answer on page 27

represented one hour, so that four squares represented four hours. Thus the length of time represented by four squares of the graph paper has been extended from four hours to five hours. It has been increased in the ratio 4:5, and correspondingly the length of paper which represents one hour has been decreased in the same ratio.

Problems 1.4

1. A survey map is marked '1 centimetre to 1 kilometre'. In what proportion does it reduce (*a*) length and (*b*) area?
2. A film projector uses film 24 mm. by 36 mm. If the size of a projected area is 10,000 times that of the film, what are the dimensions of the picture?
3. A strand of cotton 0·1 mm. thick appears to be 5 mm. thick when viewed with a microscope. What linear magnification is this?
4. A right-angled triangular piece of metal has an area of 50 sq. cm. and its shortest side is 12 cm. long. Find the corresponding length of a similar triangle if its area has been increased in the ratio 81:25.
5. A man can read one page of a book in $2\frac{1}{2}$ minutes. How long will it take a second man to read the book completely, if it has 224 pages and his reading speed compared to that of the first man is in the ratio 11:7?

Powers and roots

The production of scale models and drawings will often make it necessary to use squares and cubes of numbers and square roots and cube roots. For instance, assume that a scale model of a metal casting must be made so that the linear dimensions of the model are reduced to $\frac{1}{5}$ of those of the full-scale casting. If the volume of the casting is 1000 cubic centimetres (cm.^{3}), what is the volume of the model?

Since each of the linear dimensions is to be reduced to $\frac{1}{5}$ of the original, the area of any of its faces (e.g. a plan or an elevation) will be reduced to $(\frac{1}{5})^2$, that is to $\frac{1}{25}$ of the original area. Similarly the volume of the model will be $(\frac{1}{5})^3$, i.e. $\frac{1}{125}$, of the volume of the casting. Thus the volume of the model is $\frac{1000}{125}$ (= 8) cm^3.

Alternatively, you might have been asked how to reduce the linear dimensions so that the volume will be reduced to some stated amount. In order to reduce the volume of a model of this casting from 1000 cubic cm. to 10 cubic cm., that is 100 times, the linear dimensions have to be reduced by the cube root of 100, that is by about 4·642. Thus if the dimensions of one face were $4\frac{3}{8}$ cm. (4·375) by $12\frac{1}{8}$ cm. (12·125), they would be reduced to $\dfrac{4\cdot375}{4\cdot642}$ and $\dfrac{12\cdot125}{4\cdot642}$, that is to approximately 0·942 cm. by 2·611 cm. In order to solve problems like this, we must be able to find the square roots and cube roots of numbers.

The tediousness of the usual method for finding square roots will soon convince you that this is a good reason for including it under the heading of 'unnecessary mathematics' referred to earlier. This is especially true since books giving square root tables are commonly available. However, such tables give two numbers for each square root. Hence for 2975 the numbers 1724 and 5455 are given. Now a rough check shows that the square root of 2975 must be a little more than 50, so that 54·55 is the correct result. The square root of 297·5, however, can be seen to be about 17, because $17^2 = 289$. Here, then, the correct result is 17·24. Thus, we see that the position of the decimal point and the choice of the two numbers given in the tables must be fixed by making a rough check.

The position regarding cube roots is not so good, for tables of these are less common. How then was the cube root of 100 found to be 4·642 in the previous example? Clearly $4^3 = 64$ and $5^3 = 125$, so the correct result must lie between 4 and 5. Similarly we could find that it lies between 4·6 and 4·7. A method of this sort is of great value as a check on other methods to eliminate errors in placing the decimal point and in the more significant digits but it is too tedious to use this process as the sole method for obtaining cube roots. A better method is to use logarithms.

Logarithms

In discussing squares and cubes you may have wondered whether we could write $4^{1\cdot5}$ in the same way as we write 4^2 and 4^3. Such *non-integral indices* do have a meaning. For example, when the index is a pure fraction such as $\frac{1}{2}$ or $\frac{1}{3}$, it is taken to mean the root of the number with which it is used. Thus, $4^{\frac{1}{2}}$ means the square root of 4 and $27^{\frac{1}{3}}$ is the cube root of 27. Hence, we may write

$$\sqrt{4^3} = 4^{\frac{3}{2}} = 4^{1\cdot5}$$

so that the index, 1·5, is obtained as a result of taking the square root of the cube of a number. The well known 'three-halves power law' in electronics is an example of an application of this. However, it will be tedious to try and solve problems of this sort by trial and error methods unless, as here, the figures are very easy. Thus $4^{1\cdot5}$ is easily seen to be 8, but it is not so easy to evaluate $4^{1\cdot9}$.

Consider the equation

$$10^3 = 1000$$

This is usually stated as 'ten cubed equals 1000' but it would be equally true to read it as 'three is the power to which 10 must be raised to equal 1000'. Similarly, 2 is the power to which 10 must be raised to equal 100. The use of the powers of 10 in this way is important. A third way of expressing this same fact is that the logarithm of 1000 to the base of 10 is 3. This is usually written as

$$\log_{10}1000 = 3$$

This statement is another, often more useful, way of writing $10^3 = 1000$.

Similarly,

$$\log_{10} 100 = 2$$

We could, in the same way, write $4^{\frac{3}{2}} = 8$ as

$$\log_4 8 = \tfrac{3}{2}$$

but since most of our calculations are carried out on a scale of 10 it will be easier to confine ourselves to a system in which the logarithms have a base of 10. From the examples already stated it can be seen that, for instance, $10^{\frac{5}{2}}$ must lie between 10^2 and 10^3, that is, between 100 and 1000. Thus the square root of 10^5 read from tables (that is, $10^{\frac{5}{2}}$) $= 316 \cdot 2$. This may be written in the logarithmic form as $\log_{10} 316 \cdot 2 = 2 \cdot 5$.

Now our purpose is not to construct a table of logarithms by making such calculations. This has already been done, and the tables are commonly available.

However, it is worth pointing out here that a logarithm usually consists of one or more digits to the left of the decimal point (this part of the logarithm is called the *characteristic*) and other digits to the right of the point (known collectively as the *mantissa*). The characteristic of the logarithm of 1000 is 3 and since the logarithm is exactly 3, the mantissa is zero. It is always the case that in finding the logarithm of a number, the characteristic is one less than the number of digits to the left of the decimal point in the original number. Thus, in finding that $\log_{10}316\cdot2 = 2\cdot5$, the characteristic is found to be 2 and the mantissa is 0·5.

Now $$10^4 = 10{,}000$$

or $$\log_{10} 10{,}000 = 4$$

Also, the square root of $10^4 = 10^{\frac{4}{2}} = 10^2$

Therefore, $$\log_{10}\sqrt{10{,}000} = 2$$

The square root of the number was found by halving the index (since to obtain the square root we use the index '$\frac{1}{2}$'). Therefore in logarithmic form we halve the logarithm to find the square root of a number. For instance, from tables, the logarithm of 64 is 1·8062. Thus we should expect the logarithm of the square root of 64, that is 8, to be half of this, 0·9031. Is this so?

Similarly, the cube root of a number can be found by dividing the logarithm of the number by 3. Now the logarithm of 100 is 2. Thus the cube root of 100 is one third of 2, that is 0·6667; the logarithm tables can then be examined to find what number has the logarithm 0·6667. It is found to be 4·642. Here the decimal point is fixed by noting that the characteristic of the logarithm is zero. It follows that there must be one digit to the left of the decimal point.

This method can be extended to deducing the value of a number when it is raised to some power. Thus 2^5 can be found by multiplying $\log_{10}2$ by 5. Since $\log_{10}2 = 0\cdot3030$, $5\log_{10}2 = 1\cdot5050$. The table is then examined for the mantissa, 0·5050, and the result 3200 is obtained. Since the characteristic is 1, there must be two digits to the left of the decimal point. So $2^5 = 32$. This is only a simple example, where the result was probably obvious from the beginning, but the same method applies to all such examples. In the same way, too, non-integral indices can be evaluated by using logarithms. Thus $5^{\frac{3}{2}}$ can be written as

$$\log_{10} (5^{\frac{3}{2}}) = \frac{3}{2} \log_{10} 5$$

$$= \frac{3}{2} 0\cdot6990$$

$$= 1\cdot0485$$

Therefore $$5^{\frac{3}{2}} = 11\cdot18$$

Problems 1.5

Evaluate the following:

1. $7^{\frac{3}{2}}$
2. $6 \cdot 5^3$
3. $4 \cdot 12^{\frac{1}{3}}$
4. $5 \cdot 214^{\frac{1}{2}}$
5. $2 \cdot 641^{\frac{1}{3}}$

6. $7^{\frac{2}{3}}$
7. $6 \cdot 42^{\frac{1}{2}} \times 8 \cdot 17^{\frac{1}{2}}$
8. $10 \cdot 42^{\frac{1}{2}} \div 9 \cdot 61^{\frac{1}{2}}$
9. $2 \cdot 964^{\frac{1}{2}} \times 6 \cdot 716^{\frac{1}{3}}$
10. $4^{1 \cdot 9}$

Applications of logarithms

The subject of logarithms was introduced in this chapter as a practical method to find the cube root of a number. We have further seen that they can be used for much more than this, so that any power of a number can be found. It must be pointed out, however, that the four-figure logarithms commonly used are nearly always only approximations themselves, so that the results we obtain when using them will also be approximate, particularly where the differences between the logarithms of each consecutive figure in the table are large.

An important application of logarithms has, so far, been overlooked. When we wish to multiply together two numbers which are themselves both powers of some other number, for instance 10, then we add their indices. Thus $10^2 \times 10^3 = 10^5$. Similarly, using the logarithmic form of this, we may say that to multiply two numbers together we must add their logarithms, so long as the logarithms are to the same base. In all the examples which we shall meet in this book, this will be so. Thus 8×4 can be solved by finding the logarithms of these numbers:

$$\log_{10} 8 = 0 \cdot 9031$$
$$\log_{10} 4 = 0 \cdot 6021$$

If these are now added, we have $\log_{10} 8 + \log_{10} 4 = 1 \cdot 5052$. Examining the table will then show that $1 \cdot 5052$ is the logarithm of $32 \cdot 01$, and since $8 \times 4 = 32 \cdot 00$ we can see the extent of the error which is introduced by using four-figure tables. The error is nearly always quite small, and occurs in the least significant figure. The method can now be extended to include problems like the one worked here.

$$5 \cdot 921^3 \times 6 \cdot 428^2$$
$$\log_{10} 5 \cdot 921 = 0 \cdot 7724$$
$$\times 3 \quad \underline{}$$

Therefore $3 \log_{10} 5 \cdot 921 = 2 \cdot 3172$ $2 \cdot 3172$

$$\log_{10} 6 \cdot 428 = 0 \cdot 8080$$
$$\times 2$$

Therefore $2 \log_{10} 6 \cdot 428 = 1 \cdot 6160$ $1 \cdot 6160$

$$3 \cdot 9332$$

Result $= 8573$

Questions 7 and 9 in problems 1.5 can be most easily solved using this method, as you will appreciate if you only used logarithms to evaluate the powers and not for the multiplication. In question 8, however, a division is involved. Just as we added logarithms to multiply the numbers they represented, so, for the same reasons, we subtract the logarithms to divide. Thus $10 \cdot 42^{\frac{1}{2}} \div 9 \cdot 61^{\frac{1}{2}}$ is solved as follows:

$$\log_{10} 10 \cdot 42 = 1 \cdot 0179$$
Therefore $\tfrac{1}{2} \log_{10} 10 \cdot 42 =$ $0 \cdot 5089$
$$\log_{10} \;\; 9 \cdot 61 = 0 \cdot 9827$$
Therefore $\tfrac{1}{2} \log_{10} \;\; 9 \cdot 61 =$ $0 \cdot 4913$
subtract $\overline{0 \cdot 0176}$
Result $= 1 \cdot 041$

What if the problem had been in the following form?

$$9 \cdot 61^{\frac{1}{2}} \div 10 \cdot 42^{\frac{1}{2}}$$

$$\tfrac{1}{2} \log_{10} \;\; 9 \cdot 61 = 0 \cdot 4913$$
$$\tfrac{1}{2} \log_{10} 10 \cdot 42 = 0 \cdot 5089$$

The subtraction is only possible if we are able to borrow from the characteristic so that one mantissa can be subtracted from the other. This gives us $0 \cdot 9824$ with a characteristic of -1. The complete logarithm is written as $\bar{1} \cdot 9824$. Then from the logarithm table we proceed as before. To find the position of the decimal point the same rule is used as previously, but since the characteristic is negative it may be easier to remember the rule for negative characteristics as *adding* 1 to the characteristic (when it is negative) to find the number of zeros which must be put between the decimal point and the most significant figure. Adding 1 to -1 here we find that there are no zeros between the decimal point and the most significant figure, and the result is $0 \cdot 9603$.

This is just what we should expect for we know that $\log_{10} 100 = 2$, $\log_{10} 10 = 1$ and so $\log_{10} 1 = 0$, $\log_{10} 0\cdot1 = \bar{1}$. Similarly, we may write $\log_{10} 0\cdot01 = \bar{2}$, $\log_{10} 0\cdot001 = \bar{3}$, etc.

As examples, consider the following problems.

1. $\dfrac{1\cdot821 \times 5\cdot946^2}{8\cdot241^3}$

$$\log_{10} 5\cdot946 = 0\cdot7742 \qquad\qquad \log_{10} 8\cdot241 = 0\cdot9160$$
$$\times 2 \qquad\qquad\qquad\qquad\qquad \times 3$$
$$\overline{1\cdot5484} \qquad\qquad\qquad\qquad\qquad \overline{2\cdot7480}$$

add $\qquad\qquad \log_{10} 1\cdot821 = 0\cdot2603$

$$\overline{1\cdot8087}$$

subtract $\qquad 3 \log_{10} 8\cdot241 = 2\cdot7480$

$$\overline{1\cdot0607}$$
$$\text{Result} = 0\cdot1150$$

2. A rectangular piece of metal must be made so that its area is $1\cdot740$ square metres. If one side is $3\cdot290$ m. long, find the length of the other side.

Let the length of the other side be l

Then $\qquad\qquad l \times 3\cdot290 = 1\cdot740$

or $\qquad\qquad l \qquad\quad = \dfrac{1\cdot740}{3\cdot290}$

$$\log_{10} 1\cdot740 = 0\cdot2405$$

less $\qquad\quad \log_{10} 3\cdot290 = \underline{0\cdot5172}$

$$\bar{1}\cdot7233$$

Hence $\qquad\quad l \qquad\quad = 0\cdot5288$ m. or $52\cdot88$ cm.

Reciprocals

Now consider the second problem again, only let us assume that the area of the sheet is exactly 1 square metre.

Here $\qquad\qquad l \times 3\cdot290 = 1\cdot000$

or $\qquad\qquad l \qquad\quad = \dfrac{1\cdot000}{3\cdot290}$

$$\log_{10} 1\cdot000 = 0\cdot0000$$

less $\qquad\quad \log_{10} 3\cdot290 = \underline{0\cdot5172}$

$$\bar{1}\cdot4828$$

Hence $\qquad\quad l \qquad\quad = 0\cdot3039$ m. or $30\cdot39$ cm.

Because the area of the sheet is numerically exactly equal to 1, the lengths of the sides (here 3·290 and 0·3039), are said to be reciprocals of each other. To obtain the reciprocal of any number, this number must be divided into 1. Thus the reciprocal of 10 is $\frac{1}{10}$, and the reciprocal of $\frac{1}{273}$ is 273.

Often, to demonstrate a scientific law, it will be necessary to plot a graph. To obtain the information from which to plot the graph experiments will be carried out, and to process the information so that it is in the correct form we will sometimes use this type of calculation.

Conclusion

In this chapter we have looked primarily at some of the mathematical methods which will be of use to us. The reader should not think that we have dealt with them all, and as scientific principles are examined which call for more powerful mathematics new methods will be introduced. At the start of the chapter a study of mathematics was compared to the foundations of a house, for it is on this that new knowledge is built. It might also be compared to a bag of tools, without which many useful tasks would remain undone. This idea has one limitation, however, for tools soon become blunt and broken in use. Mathematics will never do this, and it is only by familiarity based on constant use that success can be achieved.

Problems 1.6

1. Check the accuracy of the most significant figures and decimal places in the following calculations, and where there are errors find the correct results.

(a) $\dfrac{10 \cdot 06 \times 2 \cdot 461}{507 \cdot 6} = 4 \cdot 877$

(b) $\dfrac{6 \cdot 821}{12 \cdot 96} \times \dfrac{804 \cdot 1}{0 \cdot 182} = 2325 \cdot 3$

(c) $\dfrac{12 \cdot 86^2}{3 \cdot 42^3} = 4 \cdot 134$

(d) $84 \cdot 10^{\frac{2}{3}} = 1 \cdot 283$

(e) $\log_{10} 0 \cdot 0186 = \bar{1} \cdot 2695$

2. Solve the following, correct to four significant figures:

$$4{\cdot}96^2 \qquad 2{\cdot}84^{\frac{1}{2}} \qquad 1{\cdot}04^{\frac{1}{2}} \qquad 0{\cdot}98^{\frac{1}{2}}$$

Now find the reciprocals of these expressions.

3. A number of electronic components are labelled 22, 27, 33, 39, and 47, all $\pm$ 20 per cent. What is the range of values of each of them? These numbers represent the values of the components. The components must be sorted when manufactured into one of a series of boxes numbered as above. The components may have values from 18 to 56. Which of these boxes may be eliminated, whilst still permitting all the components to be placed in boxes?

4. Find the average of each of these sets of readings, if it is known that in each case an average result is possible. Explain whether you think sufficient readings have been obtained in each case.

(a) 2·200, 2·554, 2·679, 2·402, 2·809, 3·019, 2·596, 2·505, 3·077, 2·933, 2·891, 2·528, 2·786, 2·379, 2·624, 2·354, 2·625, 2·212, 2·663, 2·751.

(b) 81·24, 94·18, 87·96, 67·24, 68·26, 72·34, 80·81, 80·92, 90·16, 91·01.

(c) 9·284, 9·304, 9·392, 9·342, 9·286, 9·262, 9·342, 9·316, 9·218, 9·288.

Answers to questions within the text of this chapter

Page 14   Average = 39·14.
Page 18   The model has $\frac{1}{1000}$ of the volume of the original.

Chapter 2
The standards of measurement

Accuracy is of paramount importance in science, and it is therefore essential that there should be no uncertainty in the taking of measurements. In this chapter we shall be particularly concerned with the precise definition of measurement standards and the methods by which these standards are arrived at.

Great care is taken to see that the materials of which a measurement standard is made are suitable for the purpose. For example, metals expand on heating, so the metals used for a standard of length (and for sub-standards copied from it) must expand and contract as little as possible, in addition to which they should be proof against corrosion. It is consequently a wise precaution to house the standard (and sub-standards) in rooms where the temperature and humidity of the air are controlled and which are as free from dust as possible.

Accuracy of measurement is important in trade and commerce as well as in the laboratory. For this reason, sub-standards are not only kept at the National Physical Laboratory where a great deal of scientific research is carried out, but also by the local inspectors at each Weights and Measures Office. These offices are maintained by local government authorities all over the country, and the officers are empowered by law to enter property where measuring instruments are used for trade.

In the course of his duty an officer may stop a coal delivery van, check a greengrocer's scales, or examine a petrol pump. The crown and other symbols on the side of a beer glass in a public house and the impression in the soft lead insert in the base of a trader's weight are guarantees that these measures are sufficiently accurate for trading.

Sub-standards have not only been distributed to all parts of the country to act as local standards: they are also regularly returned to the Board of

Trade for checking and perhaps recalibration so that the accuracy of local standards can be maintained over long periods of time. In addition, copies of our standards are exchanged with those of other countries, so that we are able to make accurate comparisons with their units of measurement.

Length

In Britain, the standard of length was for many years the imperial yard, and carefully made copies of this are available to the public, one of these being on public display in Trafalgar Square, London. However, it was decided in 1965 that the use of the scientific standard of length, the metre, should be extended to commerce and industry as well. It is not anticipated that this change will be completed before 1975, for people are often slow to accept new ideas in well established practice.

The British imperial yard was divided into 3 parts to obtain another unit, the foot, and into 36 parts to obtain the inch, whereas the lengths based on the metre (the International Prototype Metre) are divided by powers of 10 so that the centimetre is $\frac{1}{100}$ metre and the millimetre is $\frac{1}{1000}$ metre.

This division, both here and abroad, is done by highly accurate dividing engines. These are machines which are used to scribe fine lines with a diamond-faced cutting head on a piece of metal or glass. Using a machine of this kind, the original standard of length can be accurately reproduced and then other lines drawn to divide this length into a number of shorter parts, so that a scale of very high accuracy is built up. Photographic copies can be made of this, from which, for example, master dies can be produced as a first stage in the manufacture of a scale or ruler. These dies are used to impress the scale into the plastic paint of the blank scale as a series of fine parallel grooves, which are later filled in with black so that the scale is easily visible. Manufactured in this way, the final scale can have very nearly the same accuracy as the original divided scale, whose overall length was copied from the standard. 'Rulers' are also available from some sources which have been manufactured with much less care. It cannot be expected that articles satisfactory for this work can be sold for only a few pence.

Conversion of scales

It may be useful to have some knowledge of conversion factors between British and metric units of length, particularly as feet and inches are still used in the U.S.A. Here is a simple experiment with which to make the comparison, using a good quality ruler marked in inches and millimetres. A number of straight lines can be drawn, of different lengths, and these can then be measured in both systems. By dividing the lengths of the lines, measured in millimetres, by those measured in inches the number of millimetres in one inch can be found. A table of results might look similar to that shown here in table 1, although in this case only a few readings are given. It should be noted that the American inch is slightly longer than the old British one (see question 6 in problems 2.1), but for scientific purposes one inch is taken as exactly equal to 25·40 mm.

Table 1

Length of line in inches	Length of line in millimetres	Calculation	Result
10·7	272·2	$\dfrac{272\cdot2}{10\cdot7}$	25·44
11·4	289·3	$\dfrac{289\cdot3}{11\cdot4}$	25·38
9·6	243·7	$\dfrac{243\cdot7}{9\cdot6}$	25·39
8·7	221·4	$\dfrac{221\cdot4}{8\cdot7}$	25·45
11·9	301·8	$\dfrac{301\cdot8}{11\cdot9}$	25·36
		Average result	25·40

Measurement of length

In addition to rulers and other divided scales, there are three important instruments for measuring the length of small workpieces. These are the micrometer screw gauge, the dial gauge, and the travelling microscope, the scales on all of which are produced by similar techniques. Fig. 1 shows a typical micrometer screw gauge.

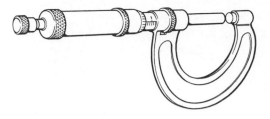

Figure 1. A micrometer screw gauge.

A typical gauge, such as the one shown here, could measure lengths up to 25 mm., the minimum reading being 0·01 mm. These gauges are in common use in the laboratory and the workshop.

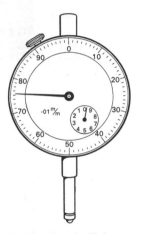

Figure 2. A dial gauge.

Fig. 2 shows a dial gauge which is used for measurements over the same range. Here, however, the workpiece is not placed between flat surfaces, as in the micrometer screw gauge, but is positioned beneath the spindle of the instrument. This spindle moves a rack so that a system of gears magnifies the movement and rotates the pointer against a calibrated scale.

A dial gauge must be fixed in a clamp so that the spindle bears on the workpiece. It is particularly useful when one side of the workpiece is quite smooth and it is required to examine variations in the other side: for example, it can be used to examine the face of an object for irregularities in its finish, provided that the object can be moved along smoothly under the spindle.

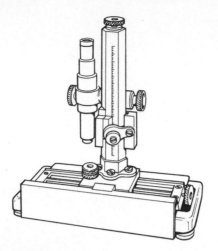

Figure 3. A travelling microscope.

Fig. 3 shows a simple travelling microscope. This is used by focusing the microscope on the point from which the measurement must be taken. The heavy base of the microscope is kept fixed while the carriage is moved to a second point. The instrument shown in the figure can be used to take measurements either vertically or horizontally without the position of the base being altered. A finely divided scale moves in conjunction with the carriage, and two separate scales are provided for the two movements.

Problems 2.1

1. If there are 25·40 mm. in 1 inch, how many inches are there in 1 metre?
2. How many square millimetres are there in 1 square inch?
3. Estimate the number of inches in 1 metre from the following pairs of results (see table 1): 41 in., 104·1 cm.; 36 in., 91·5 cm.; 52 in., 132·1 cm.; 38 in., 96·5 cm.; 34 in., 86·3 cm.
4. The pitch of an American thread on a screw is 46 to the inch. How many threads will there be in each centimetre?
5. A column of liquid in an experiment is 760 cm. high. How many inches is this?
6. If there are 25·3999 mm. in 1 inch, where the inch is defined by reference to the imperial standard yard, and the American inch is 3·7 millionths of an inch longer than the British unit, how many millimetres correspond to 1 American inch?

Present standards of length

An effort has been made recently to define standards with greater precision than before, and to make it possible to refer to an internationally agreed standard without having to rely on copies of standards which are held in separate countries. In order to do this, these new standards depend on the fundamental properties of pure substances, such as the wavelength of the light from one part of the spectrum produced in an electric discharge through a gas. An especially pure form of the rare gas krypton is used for this.

Area and volume

In problems 2.1.2 you were asked to convert an area of 1 square inch into metric units, that is, into square millimetres. The metric units of area (which are now used in the United Kingdom), such as square millimetres and square centimetres, are derived from the linear units (millimetres and centimetres) in the same way that the old British units of area (square inches and square feet) were derived from units of length. This is also true of units of volume: there are $(2.54)^3$ cubic centimetres (i.e. 16·387 cm.^{3}) in 1 cubic inch.

Of course, the older imperial measures (the gallon, quart, and pint) did not fit into this scheme so easily, since they did not correspond to any units of linear measurement. The only similar metric unit, the one which we now use, is the litre, but this is approximately 1000 cm.^{3}, so that $\frac{1}{1000}$ litre, known as a millilitre (ml.) is nearly the same as the cubic centimetre. In fact, 1 litre = 1000·028 cm.^{3} In the context of this book, these terms will frequently be taken to be interchangeable.

Mass and weight

One type of measurement which is often made in scientific laboratories (and in everyday life as well) is that of weighing, and it is well known that weight is a force. (A force opposes or attempts to oppose a body remaining at rest or continuing to move with constant speed in a straight line; see chapter 6 for further discussion on this topic.) Weight, in fact, is the force with which an object is pulled towards the Earth by gravity, so a scientist might say that the gravitational field of the Earth acts on the object and endows it with weight. If this is the case, it must be true that the force of weight is acting on the object whether it is moving or at rest.

The gravitational field of the Earth, which is responsible for giving an object weight, is not of equal strength all over the Earth's surface and in space diminishes to zero, so that we are able to talk of the 'weightlessness' of an astronaut. On the surface of the Moon, it is the Moon's gravitational field which acts on an object: this is about $\frac{1}{7}$ of that which we experience on Earth. The effect on space travellers of reduced and zero gravity has often been described.

Because of these things, how is it that we can claim to have standards of weight? Of all the entities which we measure, surely weight is the most unreliable, for a measurement made at one place may not be valid at any other place. However, it is well known that the Inspectors of Weights and Measures do compare traders' weights against their own standards, and that these are, in turn, derived from national standards.

The explanation of these apparently conflicting statements is found by examining the method of measurement and by considering what property of the object it is which is unaffected by moving from one place to another, or even by transferring it to outer space. Two properties which may be unaltered are its volume and the quantity of material, known as the mass, which is present in the object.

Everyday experience tells us that the volume of an object does not give us very much information about its weight unless we also know the nature of the substance of which it is made. We are brought back to thinking about the quantity of the particular material which is present in the object. The number of atoms or molecules (see chapter 3) present in it does not change when it is moved from one place to another: what changes is the force with which they are attracted to some larger nearby object such as the Earth or the Moon. The *mass* of the object is said to be constant.

What is the connection between mass and weight? Two objects, made of the same material, are weighed: if one of them contains twice as much material as the other, we should expect it to be twice as heavy. This should be remembered as 'weight is proportional to mass' or 'equal masses at the same place have equal weights'. It will therefore be seen that when a beam balance is used in the laboratory, and 'weights' are placed in one of the scale pans to weigh an object in the opposite pan, we are actually comparing the weight of the object with that of the pieces of metal we call 'weights'. But since this measurement is carried out with gravity acting equally on both scale pans, we are also comparing the masses of the objects.

The standards we really use are thus standards of mass, but when we use a balance to compare the weights of two objects we are also able to compare their masses.

Units of mass and weight

The British unit of mass was for many years the pound (which is still used in the U.S.A.), but we commonly spoke of a weight of one pound. This expression should be avoided, and in order to make it clear whether we are referring to the mass, which is constant, or the weight, which is not, we should say instead that an object has a mass of 1 pound or that it has a weight of 1 *pound weight*. This is not a case of splitting hairs, for science depends on accurate statements and many students have, in the past, been confused over this point.

We see that 1 lb. weight (often written as '1 lbf.') is the force which a mass of 1 lb. experiences when under standard conditions of gravity. Similarly, using the metric system, a mass of 1 kilogram (1,000 grams) results in a weight of 1 kgf. As 1 gram is a very small mass (a two-shilling piece has a mass of just over 11 grams), metric measurements of mass are often made with reference to a standard mass of 1 kg. (the International Prototype Kilogram).

Gravity

From our discussion on mass and weight we have seen that, at any one place, weight is proportional to mass. There must, therefore, be a constant of proportionality appropriate to that particular place. Sir Isaac Newton found that a force, F, such as weight, is related to the mass, M, on which this force is acting, by the statement

$$F \propto M a$$

where a is the acceleration of the object, were it to fall freely. The expression 'standard conditions of gravity' has been used, and scientists now accept that this means that the standard value of a is $980 \cdot 665$ cm.sec.$^{-2}$ (centimetres per [second]^2). 1 gf. is defined as that force which will give this acceleration to a mass of 1 gram.

Problems 2.2

1. Explain carefully whether a spring balance compares masses or weights.
2. If there are $28 \cdot 35$ g. in a liquid whose volume is 20 cm.^{3}, how many grams are there in 1 litre of it? Also, how many litres are there in a mass of 1 kg. of the liquid?
3. Why is it that we talk of 'weightlessness' and never of 'masslessness' in space?

Time

Another important laboratory measurement is that of time. Here there is no problem of conversion from one system of units to another, such as exists between the American and the metric systems, since the second is the universal primary time interval in practical use. The second was defined by the 11th General Conference on Weights and Measures in 1958 as a stated fraction of the year 1900, but here we will assume it to be $\frac{1}{86,400}$ of a mean solar day.

Systems of units of measurement

It is possible to make many different types of measurement in terms of only three basic measurements. These are mass, length, and time. For instance, the units of area are those of (length)^2, and speed is length $\div$ time. These three basic dimensions, length, mass and time, are therefore of very great importance for if we can measure them with precision many other entities can also be measured with great accuracy. As we have seen there are a number of different systems each with its own standards of mass and length. These fall basically into two groups: those which use metric units, and those (chiefly employed in the U.S.A.) which continue to use 'British' units.

We will consider first the metric systems. The c.g.s. system, as its name implies, uses the centimetre, gram, and second as its basic units of measurement: area is measured in square centimetres and speed in centimetres per second. With this system, however, the standard gravitational acceleration is approximately 981 cm.sec.$^{-2}$, so that the force of gravity on a mass of 1 gram is 981 g. cm. sec.$^{-2}$ This is called 1 dyne.

Another metric system, the M.K.S. system, uses the metre, kilogram, and second as basic units. Here standard gravitational acceleration is 9·81 m.sec.$^{-2}$ so that the force of gravity on a mass of 1 kilogram is 9·81 kg. m.sec.$^{-2}$ In the M.K.S. system, unit gravitational acceleration is called 1 newton. We have already examined an alternative force unit, the kgf.

The British systems are based on the foot, pound and second, and hence are known as f.p.s. systems. In this case standard gravitational acceleration can be found from the information already given. Thus 9·81 m.sec.$^{-2}$ can be changed to ft sec.$^{-2}$ if it is remembered that 1 metre = 39·37 inches or 39·37/12 feet (32·174 ft sec.$^{-2}$).

The use of a number of different systems of measurement is unfortunate, for some people are most familiar with grams and cubic centimetres, whilst others work in pounds and pints. Generally, it has been the physicists who have first used metric units and the engineers (formerly in Britain and now in the United States) who have used the f.p.s. system. There has been a great deal of discussion in recent years about this, particularly since there are two common metric systems, and many people would now also like to abandon the c.g.s. system and work in M.K.S. units.

These things can seldom be brought about in a hurry, and as engineers you may need to change units from one system to another. Some exercises (problems 2.3) are included to give you practice in this. The time when all mankind uses one set of standards in both scientific and everyday work is regrettably still some way off.

Problems 2.3

1. The speed of sound at sea level is about 760 m.p.h. Express this correctly in (*a*) c.g.s. units, (*b*) M.K.S. units, and (*c*) f.p.s. units.
2. The mass of water in a volume of 1 cubic foot is $62\frac{1}{4}$ lb. Express this in (*a*) c.g.s. units, and (*b*) M.K.S. units.
3. A laminated board 6 cm. × 6 cm. is coated with copper on one side to a depth of 0·05 mm. Find the volume of copper present.
4. The pages of a book measure 12·7 cm. × 17·78 cm. It has 220 pages and contains 57,000 words. What average area of paper surface is required for each word? Express your answer in square centimetres.
5. What is the mass of 1 cubic foot of sea water if 1 cm.³ of it has a mass of 1·02 g.? Give your answer in lb.

Density

In everyday language we frequently use very inexact expressions. We say, for instance, that aluminium is a light metal and lead is a heavy one, whereas we know that equal masses of lead and aluminium would have equal weights. What we are really comparing are the weights of equal volumes. When we realize this, we see that in saying lead is heavier than aluminium we mean that the mass of a certain volume of lead is greater than that of the same volume of aluminium. This argument depends on the principle that the mass of any one substance is proportional to its volume. Thus, if we double the mass of a substance, we double its volume (and, incidentally, its weight).

This can be put in another way. We may say that its mass divided by its volume is constant. This constant is called the *density* of the substance. It is a particular property of the material we are examining. For example, problems 2.3.5 could have been written as 'The density of sea water is 1·02 g. cm.$^{-3}$ (grams per cubic centimetre) . . .'

Thus, density $= \dfrac{\text{mass}}{\text{volume}}$

and is measured in g.cm.$^{-3}$ or kg.m.$^{-3}$ These are the c.g.s. and M.K.S. units respectively.

Since the idea of density has been introduced here to help make comparisons between substances, it is well to know something of the densities of some common materials. In certain cases, an estimate of the density of a substance, perhaps a metal, can easily be obtained. Its mass can be found by using a balance, since mass is proportional to weight, and if it has a regular shape its volume can also be readily calculated. If the substance does not have a regular shape the displacement method of volume determination can be employed, in which a liquid that neither chemically reacts with nor dissolves the substance is poured into a measuring cylinder and the volume of this liquid found by examining the scale on the side of the vessel. This liquid can very often be water. The substance is then lowered into the liquid and the total volume can now be found. The difference between these two readings is the volume of the substance.

Difficulties may occur if, for instance, the substance floats in the liquid. A sinker of some denser substance must then be used as shown in fig. 4, so that the combined weight of the sinker and the object will be enough to take it below the surface of the liquid. Some examples of the calculations will illustrate these points.

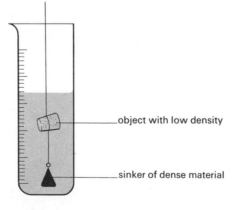

object with low density

sinker of dense material

Figure 4.   The use of a sinker in finding the density of a floating body.

A. A small cylinder made of brass was weighed. Its mass was 126·75 g. 50 cm.^{3} of water were poured into a 100 cm.^{3} measuring cylinder (it is common practice to mark measuring cylinders in millilitres: one litre is 1000·028 cm.^{3}, but we shall take the ml. as being equal to 1 cm.^{3}). When the brass was lowered so that it was completely covered by the water, the level of the water was found to be 65 cm.^{3} Thus the volume of the brass was 65 − 50, i.e. 15 cm.^{3}

Hence its density $= \dfrac{126\cdot75}{15}$

$= 8\cdot45$ g.cm.$^{-3}$

B. 47·7 g. of sugar are poured into a measuring cylinder containing 40 ml. of turpentine, in which the sugar does not dissolve. The liquid level rises to 70 ml. The volume of the sugar is therefore 30 ml.

Thus the density of the sugar is $\dfrac{47\cdot7}{30}$ g.cm.$^{-3}$, i.e. 1·59 g.cm.$^{-3}$

If it is necessary to express this result in M.K.S. units it must be multiplied by 10^6 because there are $(10^2)^3$ cm.^{3} in 1 m.^{3}, and divided by 10^3 because there are 10^3 g. in 1 kg. So the density of the sugar is 1590 kg.m.$^{-3}$

C. A slab of cork has perpendicular sides of length 20 cm., 40 cm. and 5 cm., and has a mass of 720 g. First find its density, and then explain why it is that your result is not the usually accepted value for cork (0·22 g.cm.$^{-3}$).

The volume of the cork is $40 \times 5 \times 20$ cm.^{3} = 4000 cm.^{3}

Therefore, its density is $\dfrac{720}{4000}$ g.cm.$^{-3}$ = 0·18 g.cm.$^{-3}$ (180 kg.m.$^{-3}$)

Cork frequently contains air trapped within it, so the volume we have calculated is greater than the actual volume of the cork. The result for the density of the cork based on this error is therefore too low.

Systematic errors

In chapter one the idea was discussed that if sufficient readings were obtained most of the results would lie close to some average value. It was suggested that the basis of good measurement was to take a reasonable number of readings, and provided that the majority of them lay close to this average an accurate result would be obtained. There is no reason to suppose that had we taken more readings to find the density of cork, we should have had an average value nearer to the accepted value of 0·22 g.cm.$^{-3}$ This is said to be due to a *systematic error* in our experiment.

Experimental methods must always be carefully examined in case there is any systematic error for often it cannot be removed by taking a number of readings. Notice that a systematic error was avoided in the second of the worked examples. If the sugar had merely been poured into the empty measuring cylinder, without the turpentine, the volume indicated by the surface of the sugar would have included air trapped between the sugar grains, and the calculated density would have been too small.

Problems 2.4

1. What other systematic error might occur in measuring the density of cork in the way shown in this chapter?
2. State briefly what method you would use to measure the density of the following substances: wood (e.g. deal); sand; iron (in the form of small regular cubes); common salt.
3. A barometer tube is 1 cm.^{2} in cross-sectional area and the pressure of the air supports a column of mercury in the tube 76 cm. high. If the density of the mercury is 13·6 g.cm.$^{-3}$, find the mass of mercury supported by the air pressure.
4. The density of gold is 19·3 g.cm.$^{-3}$ and that of copper is 8·9 g.cm.$^{-3}$ A wedding ring of impure gold (containing copper) has a volume of 0·75 cm.^{3} and a mass of 12 g. What is the mass of gold it contains?
5. Brass contains two parts of copper to each part of zinc (by volume). Find the density of brass if the densities of copper and zinc are 8900 and 7100 kg.m.$^{-3}$ respectively.

Chapter 3
The building bricks of matter

From the dawn of history man has sought to classify the things he sees around him in an attempt to distinguish between those substances which are fundamental to all material things and those which can be made from them. Thus we assume that there is a limited number of 'elements' which suitably combined can be used to produce any of the substances to be found on Earth. In addition, there is no reason to suppose that the rest of the universe differs from the Earth in this respect.

Elements

Aristotle defined an element as a substance into which other bodies may be decomposed, but which itself cannot be decomposed into other bodies. From this we can see that the idea of elements has been current from earliest times and was responsible for the alchemist's dream of making gold, since he argued wrongly that gold could be made from its elements. Now this same idea of elements is the foundation of modern chemistry.

Today we define an element more carefully, as a substance which cannot be broken down into more simple substances by chemical means alone. This definition is chosen because it is possible to break down such elements by using the high energy of some modern atomic particle generators.

Over 100 elements are known, either in a free state, or combined together, or manufactured artificially by nuclear devices. Of these, 88 have been found to occur naturally, whilst the remaining elements (about fifteen) are extremely radioactive and decompose very quickly into other elements as will be briefly explained at the end of this chapter. Hence, if these elements once existed naturally on the Earth, we should not expect to find them like this today.

Over 98 per cent of the Earth's crust is made up from ten of the naturally occurring elements. These are listed in table 2.

Table 2   Elements present in the Earth's crust

Percentages by weight

Oxygen	49·2	Sodium	2·7
Silicon	27·6	Potassium	2·4
Aluminium	7·5	Magnesium	1·8
Iron	4·7	Hydrogen	0·9
Calcium	3·4	Titanium	0·6

These figures are, of course, only estimates and do not take into account the nature of the Earth's core, about the content of which we know very little. The quantities of these substances which are present are very much in contrast to the abundance of the elements in space. It seems that most of the universe consists of the two lightest elements known, hydrogen and helium.

Astronomers who analyse the colour of the light from stars are able, from this alone, to discover which elements are present in them. This is because the colour of the light emitted from very hot substances is characteristic of the substances which are being heated. It is thus easier to investigate the composition of a distant star which is at a very high temperature than it is to examine the centre of our own Earth. Table 3 shows the order of distribution of the principal elements in the cosmic matter of space.

Table 3   Elements present in cosmic matter (per cent)

Hydrogen	87·5	Nitrogen	0·04
Helium	8·8	Carbon	0·02
Oxygen	0·06	Neon	0·01

Only about twenty of all the elements occur uncombined on Earth whilst the remainder are found as *compounds*, two or more of the elements combining together to form new substances. Some of these elements have been known from early history. Objects of iron, copper, silver, and gold, for example, have been found dating from earlier than 3000 B.C., but it was not then realized that they were elements. So we see that although the idea of 'elements' was intuitive—almost an inspired guess—modern science accepts this concept. What has changed, however, is the choice of substances on the list of elements. This choice is not of our making, for the elementary nature of certain substances can be shown by experiment.

One other problem has always intrigued man. If substances can be progressively broken down, will we find that there comes a time when we reach the smallest particle of a substance, or is matter continuous, so that however small our pieces are, the substance remains unchanged?

Many of the ancients thought that matter was continuous, so that if a substance, such as water, were divided into successively smaller parts, the water would still remain unchanged. However, in 1803 John Dalton suggested that matter consisted of particles. Today we would say that the smallest particle of water that can be produced, and still be water, is called a *molecule*. More generally, a molecule can be defined as a group of atoms so bonded together that they can be considered as an entity in the conditions under which they are being studied.

If we attempt to divide this molecule of water still further, the substances which we then have would be the elements of which water consists, namely hydrogen and oxygen.

This naturally raises the question of whether it is possible to subdivide an element. A molecule of hydrogen, for example, can be divided into two smaller particles. The smallest particle of an element which can exist unchanged on its own is an atom. Thus a molecule of hydrogen consists of two hydrogen atoms. Later we shall discuss the atom and its parts.

Dalton's atomic theory is now universally accepted, and a few years after his original experiments the isolation of a number of the elements gave indirect support to it.

The gas oxygen had already been isolated by Joseph Priestley in 1774, and hydrogen was produced only two years later by Cavendish. It had almost certainly been discovered by alchemists many years earlier, but their aims were such that they did not realize what they had found.

Dalton knew that hydrogen would burn in air to form water, and his own work influenced Sir Humphry Davy to isolate a number of the elements, amongst them sodium (1807), chlorine (1810), and iodine (1814).

So the list of elements grew, and with it scientific interest in the properties of these substances. Men were no longer interested in the secret ways of alchemy but publicly discussed the properties of the substances which surrounded them: the building bricks of matter.

Dalton's atomic theory was one of the important steps in understanding the way in which substances are built up. Thus it was found that when elements combine, this combination involves the union of atoms of the elements in simple numerical ratios, e.g. *two* atoms of hydrogen combine with *one* atom of oxygen to give *one* part of water. In this case, however, one atom of these gases cannot exist alone for in each of these gases two atoms are needed to form a single molecule. We therefore need four atoms of hydrogen, each molecule of hydrogen containing two atoms, to add to one molecule (two atoms) of oxygen. These then chemically combine to produce two atoms of water, a union achieved by burning hydrogen in air so that it combines with the oxygen present in the atmosphere.

We cannot, of course, weigh one atom of an element to verify this: we cannot even see it, nor can we use its density unless we know how many atoms there are in any given volume of it. Here we shall compare the weights of the elements with one of them as standard, and use this in our calculations. Some of these weights are given in table 4. The standard element, oxygen, is taken as having an atomic weight of 16, since it was originally thought that this would give the atomic weight of hydrogen as 1, and although this is not exactly correct the idea has remained.

Table 4 Atomic weights of elements

Element	Symbol	Atomic weight	Element	Symbol	Atomic weight
Carbon	C	12·01	Iron	Fe	55·85
Chlorine	Cl	35·46	Oxygen	O	16·00
Copper	Cu	63·54	Silver	Ag	107·88
Gold	Au	197·0	Sodium	Na	22·99
Hydrogen	H	1·008	Sulphur	S	32·06

The symbols in table 4 are useful in describing chemical changes. For instance, we might say that two molecules of hydrogen, each of which contains two atoms, combine with one molecule of oxygen, also containing two atoms, to form two molecules of water, each of which contains two atoms of hydrogen and one atom of oxygen. All this information is contained in the chemical equation

$$2H_2 + O_2 = 2H_2O$$

One important fact about any chemical equation is that the sum of the atomic weights on each side of the equation will always balance. In this example:

$$4 \times 1{\cdot}008 + 2 \times 16 = 2 \times 18{\cdot}016$$

The sum of the atomic weights of the elements gives the molecular weight of the compound. Here it is 18·016. These weights correspond to actual weights: in the equation 36·032 g. of water are formed from 4·032 g. of hydrogen and 32 g. of oxygen.

Problems 3.1

1. Write down an equation for the formation of carbon dioxide (CO_2) from carbon and oxygen. Note that the oxygen molecule has two atoms. What is the molecular weight of carbon dioxide?
2. Write down an equation for the action of sodium on water, in which hydrogen and sodium hydroxide (NaOH) are formed. What is the molecular weight of sodium hydroxide?
3. In question 1, what weight of carbon would have been needed to produce 100 g. of carbon dioxide?
4. The chemical formula for hydrous copper sulphate is $CuSO_4.5H_2O$, and for silver chloride is AgCl. What are their molecular weights?

In question 4 the molecular weights of two substances were found. The density of copper sulphate is 2·286 g. cm.$^{-3}$ and of silver chloride is 5·56 g. cm.$^{-3}$, which is twice this. Yet the molecular weight of copper sulphate is much greater than that of silver chloride. How is this? We have already met a similar problem in chapter 2 when we saw that density is the ratio of mass to volume. This information would seem to imply that the volume of a molecule of silver chloride is much less than that of a molecule of copper sulphate. By arguing in this way we can see there is good reason to believe that the volume of molecules differs greatly. Further, we have reason to believe that the difference in volume is not due primarily to the space occupied by the atomic nuclei, but to the space between the nuclei within the molecule.

Compounds and mixtures

We have now seen some examples of the way in which elements combine to form compounds. This should not be confused with the mere mixing of substances together. To use a familiar example, sodium is a soft metal, that can be cut with a knife, and which burns fiercely in air with a bright yellow flame and a great deal of spluttering, producing a white caustic deposit. Chlorine is a yellow-green gas with a choking odour which was used as a poison gas in the First World War. Common table salt, or to give it its chemical name, sodium chloride, is not in the least like either of these elements, yet it can be formed by burning sodium in chlorine gas. This innocuous substance is a compound, not a mixture, and so has new properties: it has a characteristic taste, and a crystal of common salt examined under the microscope will be seen to be colourless. The ability to recognize when new substances have been formed is important, the changes may not always be as startling as these, but we must be able to distinguish between compounds and mixtures.

However, we may sometimes be deceived into thinking new compounds have been formed by mixtures and the different forms which elements and compounds can have. For instance, a film of oil on a road surface looks quite unlike the oil we use in the workshop; ice and steam would not seem to be chemically the same as water, and soot appears to be no substitute for diamonds. Ice and steam are physically different forms of the compound water; soot and diamonds are different forms of the element carbon.

Problems 3.2

1. How can we distinguish between physical and chemical changes? Heat some powdered sulphur in a crucible with a lid, until the sulphur has melted. Use tongs to pour the melted sulphur into cold water. Examine both the sulphur which is in the water, and (when it has cooled) the sulphur remaining in the crucible. In what ways are they different? If each kind of sulphur is kept for a few days and then powdered, it will be found to have all the properties of the original sulphur. Are these changes physical or chemical ones?
2. Mix together thoroughly about equal volumes of iron filings and sulphur. Has any chemical change taken place? Heat the mixture in a crucible until it glows red. Allow it to cool. Has any chemical change taken place? Repeat the experiment using equal weights of iron and sulphur. In each case use a magnet to show whether any iron remains at the end of the experiment. Calculate the quantity of iron which is

necessary to ensure that all the substances are combined (assume you use 10 g. of sulphur).

3. What is the percentage by weight of copper in copper sulphate crystals ($CuSO_4.5H_2O$)?

4. A compound contains 75 per cent of carbon and 25 per cent hydrogen. By dividing each percentage by the atomic weight of the element, deduce the formula of the compound.

5. Ammonium nitrate (NH_4NO_3) is used as a fertilizer, on account of the nitrogen combined in it. What percentage by weight of nitrogen is present? (Atomic weight of nitrogen = 14.)

The atmosphere

The substances present in the atmosphere are listed in table 5.

Table 5   The constituents of the atmosphere

Substance	Percentage by volume
Nitrogen	78
Oxygen	20·98
Argon	0·94
Carbon dioxide	0·04[1]

[1]This may be as much as 1 per cent in a crowded room.

In addition to these, water vapour will be present, the amount (1 to 3 per cent) depending on the nature of the weather; dust and other gases such as sulphur dioxide may also occur, especially in industrial towns. The air is a good example of a mixture of substances, but it can also take part in chemical reactions.

Dust in the air

It might at first seem that the dust in the air is unimportant, but in fact it is on this dust that water vapour condenses. You will probably have noticed how much better visibility is after a rainstorm has laid the dust which was in the air. Those parts of the world where there is very little dust in the atmosphere have, as we might expect, good visibility, but often they also have a very low annual rainfall even though there may be water vapour present: this is because there is no dust in the air to encourage the formation of drops of rain. Over such areas it has sometimes been possible to produce rain by releasing silver iodide or solid carbon dioxide from aircraft.

In the upper atmosphere, where there is very little dust, the disturbance caused by a passing aircraft can bring about condensation of the water vapour in a trail behind it.

Chemical reactions with air

We have all seen rusted ironwork, and a simple experiment will show the part which the air plays in causing this. Take three test tubes and put in each a few bright iron nails. In the first tube place some freshly boiled water, in the second put some water through which air has been bubbled. Nothing other than the nails is put in the third tube. The tubes should then be sealed with tight-fitting rubber bungs. Thus, as well as the nails, one of the tubes contains water, the second contains water and some dissolved air, and the third has only air in it. Signs of rust should appear in a few days in only one of the tubes. From this experiment you can deduce the conditions which are necessary for rusting to take place.

The substance in the air which causes rusting is oxygen, for rust is an oxide of iron. Oxygen and carbon dioxide are responsible for the corrosion of copper, and the green coloration of copper roofs is due to the formation of copper carbonate (the chemical changes which actually take place are more complex than this equation implies):

$$2Cu + 2CO_2 + O_2 = 2CuCO_3$$

The sulphur dioxide in town air combines with water (e.g. rain) to form sulphurous acid:

$$SO_2 + H_2O = H_2SO_3$$

This acid attacks the stonework of buildings (calcium carbonate) forming soluble salts which are washed away in the rain, so that the stone begins to crumble.

Other substances often exposed to the open air are not so easily attacked.

Nickel, chromium and aluminium are typical examples. Aluminium has a very thin layer of hard aluminium oxide on its surface which prevents oxygen in the air oxidizing the remainder of the metal. It is possible to remove this by scraping the surface of the metal in the presence of mercury, e.g. by scratching the surface of a piece of aluminium with a sharp knife and rubbing some mercury well into the scratches. The reaction which takes place is between the oxygen which is in the air and the aluminium; the mercury is not changed at all, but its presence is necessary in order to speed up the reaction. If you have managed to get a vigorous reaction in which plenty of aluminium oxide is formed you will notice that the metal becomes warm, even to the point where it is too hot to hold. This is an example of an exothermic reaction because during the course of it heat is given out.

Combustion

There are some substances that do not react with oxygen at normal temperatures, but which when sufficiently warmed are involved in exothermic reactions; the heat given out is sufficient to warm more of the substance, so that the reaction can continue. Often more heat is available than is necessary for the reaction itself, such a condition being called combustion or burning.

When wood is heated its complex molecules are broken down into simpler molecules. Tar, oils and gas are formed which are readily combustible (i.e. they combine with oxygen). Of course, when wood is burnt this cannot easily be seen, but if some wood is heated as shown in fig. 5, the substances which take part in combustion can be readily identified.

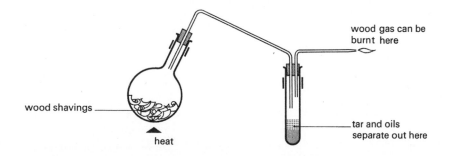

Figure 5. Apparatus for heating wood and separating the products.

When combustion takes place, energy is released, often in the form of heat. The flickering flame of a candle is the visible sign that candlegrease is being burnt to form carbon, carbon dioxide, and water vapour, not very much heat energy being produced. The destructive inferno of a blazing building, on the other hand, often gives off so much heat energy that metal objects are melted, nearby trees and buildings set on fire, and the firemen are prevented from approaching the conflagration.

Since chemical changes have occurred, the volume taken up by the products of combustion may be vastly different from the original volume of the combustible material. For instance, in the internal combustion engine, the carburettor mixes air and petrol vapour which then pass into the cylinders. When it is fired by an electric spark, the sudden change in pressure in the cylinders moves the piston, so increasing the volume within the cylinder. The products of combustion include carbon, carbon monoxide and water vapour.

Atomic structure

So far we have seen that the building bricks of compounds are molecules, and that molecules consist of atoms, combining together in simple proportions. When a molecule of a compound is broken down into the elements of which it is composed, there are considerable physical and chemical changes so that the elements are often very different from the compounds in which they are found. All this tells us nothing about the structure of the atom except that we might suppose the change in properties between the atom and its parts to be as great as the change in properties between compounds and elements. This is indeed so.

In 1815 William Prout suggested (Prout's hypothesis) that the atomic weights of the elements were all exact multiples of the atomic weight of hydrogen and that hydrogen was the primary element (a very attractive hypothesis since many of the atomic weights were approximately multiples of that of hydrogen) but it was not until the experiments of Rutherford and his co-workers that Niels Bohr was able to put forward the rudiments of the atomic theory. Only then were chemists able to understand the reason for the combination of atoms.

Rutherford had suggested that the atom consisted of a nucleus, in which most of the mass of the atom was concentrated, around which much lighter particles orbited like planets around the Sun—with one difference, however. The forces which hold the planets on their courses are gravitational, but atomic forces are electrostatic in origin. In the case of hydrogen only one particle, or electron as it is now called, moves around the nucleus.

The electron is found to carry a negative electric charge (see chapter 5) and since the atom itself is uncharged, there must be a corresponding positive charge on the nucleus. This is due to the positively charged proton. Thus hydrogen has a single electron orbiting around a single proton.

We now know that there are two other substances having the chemical properties of hydrogen, but with atomic weights of 2 and 3. These are still forms of the element hydrogen and are said to be examples of *isotopes* of hydrogen. The isotope with an atomic weight of 2, deuterium, must still have the one orbital electron which is characteristic of hydrogen, and one proton to balance the charge of the electron. But since it has double the atomic weight there must be another particle in the nucleus. This uncharged particle is the neutron. For the same reasons tritium (atomic weight = 3) has one proton, two neutrons, and one electron.

Now we can apply this reasoning to the other elements. The second lightest is helium with an atomic weight of 4: it has two electrons with two protons to balance their charge, and in addition there must be two neutrons to give the correct atomic weight. The third element, lithium, has two isotopes of atomic weights 6 and 7 respectively. Lithium will thus have three electrons, and so three protons, but in one isotope three neutrons and in the other four (fig. 6) are needed to give the correct atomic weights.

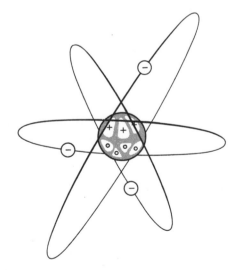

Figure 6. Diagrammatic representation of the lithium-7 atom.

This is, of course, only a very simple introduction to atomic structure, but it does give us the reasons for some elements having non-integral atomic weights. For example, the atomic weight of lithium is 6·94. Now this is much nearer 7 than 6, so we should expect to find that the isotope of lithium with an atomic weight of 7 was present to a larger extent than the other one in ordinary lithium. In fact, in naturally occurring lithium there is 92 per cent of lithium-7 and 8 per cent of lithium-6. So we see that non-integral atomic weights were not, as Prout thought, the result of errors in the calculations of chemists, but due to the presence of various isotopes which they failed to recognize. Elements consisting of one isotope only have weights, as Prout said, that are almost exact multiples of the atomic weight of hydrogen. This theory also enables us to see what the effect will be of splitting the nucleus of the atom. Elements with a large number of protons and neutrons in the nucleus will be split up into elements with fewer nuclear parts, and so with lower atomic weights. Perhaps the dream of the alchemist has its counterpart in present-day chemistry after all!

Problems 3.3

1. Is air a compound or a mixture? Give reasons for your answer.
2. How can iron be prevented from rusting without coating the metal?
3. What is understood by (a) an exothermic reaction, and (b) the opposite of this, an endothermic reaction?
4. Carry out experiments to examine the substances which take part in the combustion of (a) wood and (b) coal.
5. What is understood by Prout's hypothesis? In what ways were his assumptions (a) true, and (b) false?
6. Fluorine has an atomic weight of 19 and its atomic number is 9. What is its atomic structure?
7. Neon has 10 neutrons in its nucleus. Its atomic weight is 20. How many electrons are there around the nucleus?
8. Find, to a reasonable approximation, the molecular weight of (a) hydrogen, and (b) air.

Chapter 4
Heat and temperature

What is heat and how is it measured? In chapter 3 we looked briefly at the historical development of some aspects of chemistry. You may have thought that if the atomic theory had been developed earlier, many false trails would have been avoided. This is certainly true about the study of heat, which was at one time thought to be an element, and later to be a fluid: neither of these ideas are accepted today. In this chapter we shall be concerned only with current ideas on the nature of heat.

Heat as energy

We now know that heat is a form of energy, and it is from this point of view that the effects which heat produces can most easily be explained. Take 100 g. of ice from a refrigerator and crush it to a fine powder. Return it to the refrigerator, and make sure that it is kept very cold. When you are ready to commence the experiment, pack it into a vacuum flask with a thermometer and a heating element as shown in fig. 7.

The heating coil can be conveniently connected to a switch and the low voltage winding of a transformer or to an accumulator. This arrangement will ensure that when the electrical power is switched on, the ice is heated at a constant rate. If required, a stirrer can be included with the apparatus, so that as water forms the whole of the contents of the flask can be kept at the·same temperature. It should be possible to allow the heating to continue until the water is quite warm. If there is sufficient time, it should be possible to boil the water.

If, from the start of the experiment, frequent readings of the thermometer are taken at regular recorded intervals of time, you will have data from which to plot a graph of temperature against time. Carry out the experiment, plot the graph, and attempt to answer the following questions about the experiment.

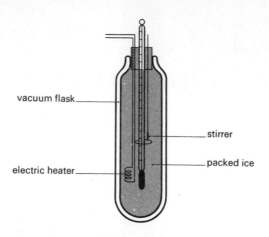

Figure 7. Heating ice in a vacuum flask.

Problems 4.1

1. Why was a vacuum flask used?
2. What would have been the drawback of using an ordinary laboratory glass beaker? How would this have altered the graph?
3. How does the graph show that the energy being supplied to heat the water was constant? Was this same energy being supplied when the ice was melting? Does the graph show this?
4. In what ways would the graph be different if the contents of the flask were not stirred?
5. What changes in temperature took place whilst the ice was melting?
6. What changes in temperature took place whilst the water was boiling?

This experiment was carefully arranged so that there was a constant supply of electrical energy to the contents of the flask. The purpose of the electrical supply was to force a current to flow through the heating element so that it would become warm, changing the electrical energy into heat. This is just one experiment which helps us to see that heat is really a form of energy and that energy of one kind (electricity) can be changed into energy of another kind (heat). We will return to this point later.

This experiment also shows us that one of the effects of heat is to *change the state* of substances. In this case ice was changed to water and subsequently to steam. Heat energy can often be used to change a solid to a liquid or a liquid to a gas.

There is one difficulty in all this. The electrical energy was producing heat at a constant rate. We know that this was all being supplied to the contents of the flask because a vacuum flask lets very little heat escape, and because the slope of the graph was constant once the ice had melted. But while the ice was melting the temperature did not rise at all. How could it be true that heat energy was being supplied to the ice if its temperature did not rise? Again, if you were able to continue the experiment until the water began to boil you would find that at this point also the temperature ceased to rise, and in fact would remain constant all the while that the water was boiling. The results of the experiment may be shown in a graph similar to that of fig. 8.

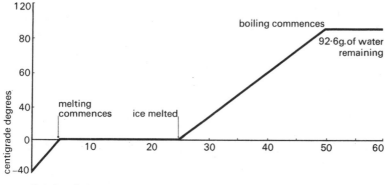

Figure 8. Latent heat. Graph to show what happens when ice is heated, turning first into water and then into steam.

The explanation is that energy is required to change the state of a substance. In this case, the heat energy was used to change the ice to water. This happened at 0°C. (273° Kelvin). Only when this change had been completed was the heat available to raise the temperature of the water. For this reason it is convenient to describe the heat energy as 'sensible heat' when it is raising the temperature of a substance, and 'latent heat' or 'hidden heat' when it is changing the state of a substance.

Measurement of heat

We have now seen some of the effects of heat and we must examine the ways in which heat can be measured. In the experiment, 100 g. of ice were used, so that after heating for a short time the flask contained 100 g. of water. Now, the amount of energy used to raise the temperature of the water depends on

(a) the mass of water present and

(b) the temperature rise through which the water is heated.

From this we can make the following definition:

The energy required to raise 1 g. of water through a change of temperature of 1 centigrade degree is 1 calorie.

Thus, if 100 g. of water in the experiment are heated from 15°C. to 35°C., a change of 20 deg. C., the energy required will be $100 \times 20 = 2000$ calories. Also, if this took 5 minutes, as shown in fig. 8, the rate of heating would have been $\frac{2000}{5} = 400$ calories per minute.

Now this rate is constant throughout, so that during the time that the ice was melting (20 minutes in fig. 8) 400 calories per minute were also being supplied to the ice. Thus it took $400 \times 20 = 8000$ calories to melt 100 g. of ice without any change in temperature or $\frac{8000}{100}$ calories for 1 gramme. Hence, we say that the latent heat of ice is 80 calories per gram.

The graph also shows that the temperature of the water remains at 100°C. while it is boiling. If, after 10 minutes, 92·6 g. of water remain in the flask, then 7·4 g. have boiled away. We have already found that in 10 minutes 4000 calories of heat have been supplied to the water without any change in temperature taking place. Therefore $\frac{4000}{7 \cdot 4} = 540$ calories, and we can say that the latent heat of steam is approximately 540 calories per gram.

Finally, the first part of the graph showed the temperature of the ice rising until melting commenced. You will see that the slope of this part of the graph was steeper than when the temperature of the water was rising. This is because ice needs less heat to raise its temperature than does the same mass of water.

From fig. 8 we can see that the temperature of the ice rose 40 deg. C. in 5 minutes for the supply of 2000 calories. Thus 20 calories would be needed to raise the temperature of 1 g. of ice through 40 deg. C., or 0·5 calories to raise 1 g. of ice through 1 deg. C. Thus, in comparison with water, which by definition needs 1 calorie per gram per deg. C., we may say that the *specific heat* of ice is 0·5 cal. g.$^{-1}$ deg.$^{-1}$C. (calories per gram per degree centigrade rise).

Specific heat

Nearly all substances require much less heat than water to raise their temperature, so that specific heats are almost always less than unity. Some typical specific heats are shown in table 6.

Table 6 Specific heats of some common substances

Calories per gram per degree centigrade rise

Air	0·24	Olive oil	0·48
Brass	0·09	Sand	0·20
Chalk	0·21	Sea water	0·94
Copper	0·09	Solder	0·04

Problems 4.2

1. What is the scientific explanation of the saying 'The sea heats and cools more slowly than the land'? Under similar atmospheric conditions, after a short warm spell of weather, which would be warmer, a fresh water lake or a sea-water inlet?

2. Heat a small known quantity of golden syrup in a beaker and at a suitable temperature (about 80°C.) pour it into a measured quantity of water in a vacuum flask. From the initial and final temperatures of the water, find the specific heat of the golden syrup.

3. If lead melts at 327°C., its specific heat is 0·03 cal. g.$^{-1}$ deg.$^{-1}$C. and its latent heat is 5 cal. g.$^{-1}$, what heat will be given out when 10 g. of molten lead at 327°C. is poured into a large block of ice? How much ice will be melted?

4. The latent heat of liquid ammonia is 108 cal. g.$^{-1}$ It boils at −75°C. and the gas has a specific heat of 0·5 cal. g.$^{-1}$ deg.$^{-1}$C. Sulphur dioxide boils at −10°C. and has a latent heat of 96 cal. g.$^{-1}$ Its specific heat is 0·2 cal. g.$^{-1}$ deg.$^{-1}$C. From this information estimate the heat which must be removed from 1 g. of each of these gases in order to liquefy it, if the gases are initially at 0°C. Name one industrial application based on these properties of these gases.

5. A vacuum flask contains 100 g. of water at 20°C. A 10 g. piece of brass is heated in a gas flame and then plunged into the water. If the final temperature of the water was 23°C., find the temperature of the flame.

6. The following results, similar to that of question 5, were obtained from a series of experiments performed in a laboratory by a number of students.

374°C. 365°C. 400°C. 325°C. 410°C. 344°C. 360°C. 338°C. 342°C. 370°C.

What is the most likely value for the temperature of the flame, and with what accuracy should it be stated?

7. An electric heater supplies heat at a constant rate to a vacuum flask which contains 40 g. of ice and some water. After 26 minutes the temperature is 8°C. and after 41 minutes it is 20°C. Use these results to draw a graph showing how long it took the ice to melt, the rate of heating, and how long it was after heating commenced before the water began to boil.

Heat calculations

Problems such as question 5 above are most easily solved if one considers the heat gained by the water and the heat lost by the piece of brass. If, for instance, a 20 g. piece of copper is heated to 300°C., the heat it possesses can be taken as equal to:

$$\text{mass} \times \text{specific heat} \times \text{temperature}$$

Thus it is: $20 \times 0.09 \times 300$ calories

It will, in fact, be greater than this because it possesses heat even at 0°C. so that we should write:

$$\text{heat} = (\text{mass} \times \text{specific heat} \times \text{temperature}) + \text{a constant}, C.$$

However, if this piece of copper is dropped into some liquid, for instance into 80 g. of olive oil, the oil will be warmed (say from 20°C. to t°C.). The heat now possessed by the copper =

$$(\text{mass} \times \text{specific heat} \times \text{temperature}) + C$$

so that the change of heat =

$$\text{mass} \times \text{specific heat} \times \text{change in temperature}.$$

Here this is $20 \times 0.09 \times (300 - t)$

i.e. $540 - 1.8t$ calories.

This heat has been lost by the copper, and from the information given the olive oil has gained heat:

$$\text{mass of oil} \times \text{specific heat} \times \text{change in temperature}$$

That is $80 \times 0.48 \times (t - 20)$

i.e. $38.4t - 768$ calories.

If the heat lost by the copper has been given up completely to the oil, these results can be equated as follows:

$$540 - 1 \cdot 8t = 38 \cdot 4t - 768$$

or $\qquad 40 \cdot 2t = 1308$

Therefore $\qquad t = 32 \cdot 5°C.$

There are, however, two problems which we have so far not taken into account. The first of these is that the oil must be held in some container (for instance a copper can) which will also become warmed. Let us examine how this may affect the final temperature. We will assume that the can has a mass of 100 g.

The heat lost by the piece of hot copper may still be written as

$$540 - 1 \cdot 8t \text{ calories}$$

but this heat is now shared between the oil, which still receives

$$38 \cdot 4 \ (t - 20) \text{ calories}$$

and the copper can. This receives

$$100 \times 0 \cdot 09 \times (t - 20)$$

or $\qquad 9 \ (t - 20) \text{ calories}$

Thus, the total heat gained is

$$(38 \cdot 4 + 9) \ (t - 20)$$

or $\qquad 47 \cdot 4(t - 20)$

or $\qquad 47 \cdot 4t - 948 \text{ calories}$

The new equation is, therefore

$$540 - 1 \cdot 8t = 47 \cdot 4t - 948$$

or $\qquad 49 \cdot 2t = 1488$

so that $\qquad t = 30 \cdot 2°C.$

As we should expect, the final temperature is lower, since energy had to be used to warm the copper can as well as the olive oil.

The other problem is that whilst the experiment was being carried out, heat energy was being used in heating up the air in contact with the can and its contents. Also, the 20 g. piece of copper would lose heat to the air whilst it was dropping into the oil. The earlier experiments described in this chapter were carried out in a vacuum flask which, whilst open to the air at its neck, lost very little heat through its sides.

Heat some water to about 80°C. and pour equal volumes into (a) an open vacuum flask, (b) a corked vacuum flask, (c) an open glass beaker, (d) a beaker surrounded by cotton wool, and (e) a metal can. In each case record the temperature every 5 minutes. How many calories were being lost in the first 5 minutes from each of them? . . . in the second period of 5 minutes? . . . in the third? From these experiments find which loses heat most quickly. Is heat lost more quickly at high temperatures? After how long, and at what temperatures, is the rate of loss of heat from the metal can and from the open flask equal?

Problems 4.3

1. Heat some naphthalene in a test tube until it is molten. Place a thermometer in the liquid. Place the test tube in a clamp so that it can be allowed to stand without touching it. Record the temperature of the liquid at regular intervals, and from this sketch a graph showing its temperature until it becomes solid. Explain the shape of the curve.

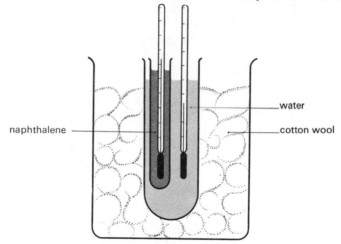

naphthalene

water

cotton wool

Figure 9.   Apparatus for recording the temperature during the cooling of a liquid.

Repeat the experiment, but when the naphthalene is about to solidify, place it in a larger tube of water as shown in fig. 9, until it is just solid, and the temperature has again begun to fall. What can you estimate from the rise in temperature of the water?

2. The latent heat of ether at room temperature is 86 cal. g.$^{-1}$ Air is bubbled through some ether so that it evaporates quickly. The ether is held in a shiny silver bottle which rapidly becomes covered with moisture as the ether evaporates. Explain this. What would you expect to happen if (*a*) the bottle of ether were held in the hand, and (*b*) the bottle of ether were standing on a wet desk?

3. A piece of metal with a mass of 100 g. and a specific heat of 0·11 cal. g.$^{-1}$ deg.$^{-1}$C. was heated to 100°C. It was then quickly transferred to a piece of ice at 0°C. and 13·75 g. of water were formed. From this, find the latent heat of ice.

4. 11,000 calories of heat are used to heat a metal beaker whose specific heat is 0·10 cal.g.$^{-1}$ deg.$^{-1}$C. and which weighs 250 g. If the beaker contains 100 g. of ice at 0°C. and the final temperature of the beaker and its contents is 20°C., find the heat gained from, or lost to, the surroundings.

5. A man makes tea by pouring 250 g. of boiling water into a metal tea pot of mass 150 g. and specific heat 0·1 cal. g.$^{-1}$ deg.$^{-1}$C., initially at 20°C. What is the final temperature of the tea if the heat absorbed by the leaves is ignored?

Mechanical equivalent of heat

If heat is a form of energy, it should be possible to carry out a simple experiment to measure how much mechanical energy is needed to produce a given amount of heat energy. When an object falls due to gravity acting on it, it gains energy. If this mechanical energy can be changed to heat energy then some connection between them can be found.

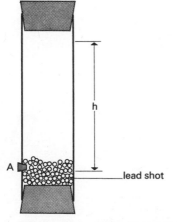

Figure 10. Apparatus for measuring the mechanical equivalent of heat.

Fig. 10 represents a cardboard tube about 1 metre in length. Its ends are closed by corks or rubber bungs. A small bung, A, is provided so that when required a thermometer can be inserted into the tube. A known mass of lead shot is placed in the tube as shown in the figure. The object of the experiment is to invert the tube a large number of times so that when the lead shot falls in the tube it will gain energy which, when the lead comes to rest at the end of the tube, will be transformed into heat.

First measure h, the average distance fallen by the shot. Then the work done, w, by a mass, m, falling a distance, h, is given by

$$w = mgh$$

where g is the acceleration due to gravity.

This work will be done every time the tube is inverted, so that if it is inverted n times, the total work, W, is given by

$$W = nmgh$$

This total work will be changed to heat and if it is assumed that this heat is given almost entirely to the lead shot, the heat gained can be calculated. Remember to remove the thermometer after taking the temperature of the lead shot at the start of the experiment. It can later be replaced to find the final temperature of the lead.

The heat gained, H, is given by $ms(t_2 - t_1)$ calories, where m is the mass, s the specific heat of the lead, t_2 the final temperature and t_1 the temperature at the start.

In a typical experiment using a tube containing 200 g. of lead and with h equal to 0·1 metre, the tube was inverted 500 times.

Each time the tube was inverted the work done was

$$w = 0·2 \times 9·81 \times 0·1*$$
$$= 0·1962 \text{ joules}$$

so that the total work,

$$W = 500 \times 0·1962$$
$$= 98·1 \text{ joules}$$

*Note that 200 g. is written here as 0·2 kg. and 100 cm. as 0·1 m., since M.K.S. units are used to obtain the work in joules.

The temperature at the start of the experiment was 17·6°C. and at the end was 21·5°C., a rise of 3·9 deg. C.

Thus, $H = 200 \times 0.03 \times 3.9$

$$= 23.4 \text{ calories}$$

In this experiment, 98·1 joules were equivalent to 23·4 calories or $\frac{98.1}{23.4}$ joules per calorie. This result of 4·2 joule cal.$^{-1}$, known as the mechanical equivalent of heat, is also applicable to the transfer of electrical energy to heat.

In many cases where work is done, heat is produced. Water at the bottom of a waterfall is slightly warmer than at the top. The brakes of a car become warm when they are continuously applied as the vehicle goes down hill. A piece of metal becomes heated when worked with a file, and a blunt drill will make a workpiece quite hot. In all these cases, 1 calorie of heat is produced for every 4·2 joules of energy used in this way.

It is worth noting that since a definite quantity of heat is equivalent to some corresponding amount of work, and both of them are forms of energy, then there must be similar relationships between other forms of energy. We should consequently expect to find that the total amount of energy available (in whatever form) must be constant. One result of this is that it is only possible to raise the temperature of a body by the application of external energy to it, or by converting energy from some other form which it possesses into heat energy. Heat cannot be taken from a cool body to a hot one without some external force: in a refrigerator, for example, heat is taken from its contents (which are cool) to the warmer outside air, but to do this it is necessary to use the energy obtained from gas or electricity.

Problems 4.4

1. Estimate the rise in temperature of water falling 100 m. over a waterfall.
2. If all the light from a 100 joule photoflash bulb could be converted into heat energy, what rise in temperature would it cause in a piece of copper whose mass is 1 g.?
3. A 400 g. piece of copper is drilled by a blunt drill so that its temperature is raised from 20°C. to 160°C. Find in joules the work done in heating the block. Why is it that, in practice, the result will be greater than you have calculated?

4. Find the electrical power in watts required to produce the heating shown in the graph of fig. 8 (1 watt = 1 joule sec.$^{-1}$).
5. A 60 watt electric soldering iron has a copper bit of mass 150 g. initially at 20°C. If the iron is accidentally switched on in circumstances in which there are negligible heat losses from the iron, how long will it be before the bit temperature is 200°C.?

Friction

One of the commonest instances of mechanical work being converted to heat is friction. Some examples have already been quoted to illustrate this. Since a machine is often intended to have a maximum rate of working, it can be seen that if part of the available work is being converted into heat, the amount of work still available in using the machine will be reduced. Friction thus reduces the efficiency of a machine.

Friction is caused by the motion of one rough surface upon another, so it can be reduced if lubricants are used to make the surfaces slip more easily over each other. Lubricants and coolants should, however, be carefully distinguished. In using a mechanical saw, for example, a lubricant would reduce the ability of the saw to cut the metal, but a coolant would readily take away the heat from the blade and so preserve its cutting edge.

Expansion

Heat, as we have seen, is a form of energy, and we can now consider the effect on the molecules of a substance of giving heat to it. We have also seen that there is a close link between heat and mechanical energy.

In chapter 3 some account was given of the nature of molecules, and the forces within them. Here we shall examine briefly the forces between molecules. In some substances molecules are held in a regular pattern spaced at definite distances from their neighbours and bonded together by the ability to share the orbits of certain electrons. Such substances are crystals. It might help to picture them as a kind of highly ordered frog-spawn, the eggs being the molecules and the jelly the space between them, or like an army on parade, each soldier the regulation distance from his neighbours. More often this order is broken down by flaws and the substance is said to be granular. In some cases all order is missing and the substance is said to be amorphous (without form). Some powders are like this.

However, each molecule is not held immovable in its position by the surrounding molecules. It stores heat energy as motion, vibrating about its central position as though held by rubber bands joining it to adjacent particles. One impact from outside the substance and all the particles are set in motion. This impact represents the work done on the substance and the resulting motion is observed as heat. The motion produced is not identical in all the particles. Visualize the soldiers at attention on a barrack square: imagine that each is told to jump a number of times in the air in the place where he stands. The jumping varies from one soldier to another within the boundaries set by the other troops, but there is an average jump typical of the individual energy exhibited by the soldiers. The average energy of the molecules is a measure of the heat energy given to them.

All this motion causes the molecules to move slightly farther apart. We say that the substance expands, and since the extent of the movement depends on the extent of the heat energy, the expansion is directly proportional to the increase in temperature and to the number of molecules involved.

Thus the expansion, x, of a piece of material of length l, which is raised in temperature from t_1 to t_2, is given by

$$x \propto l(t_2 - t_1)$$

If this proportionality is to become an equation some constant must be introduced which applies to the substance being considered. This is necessary because molecules differ from one chemical substance to another, resulting in varying expansions.

Thus, $x = a\,l(t_2 - t_1)$

where a is the coefficient of linear expansion.

Again, $a = \dfrac{x}{l(t_2 - t_1)}$

and so is measured per degree centigrade.

Some typical coefficients are given in table 7. They will be required for use in later problems.

Table 7   Coefficients of linear expansion of some common substances
(all × 10⁻⁶ deg.⁻¹ C., i.e. copper 16·7 × 10⁻⁶ deg.⁻¹ C.)

Copper	16·7	Lead	29·0
Glass	9	Nickel steel (48% nickel)	9
Invar steel	0·92	Phosphor bronze	16·9
Iron	10·5	Solder	24

When the heat energy given to the molecules becomes intense enough the average energy of the molecules is sufficient to cause a partial break-down in the bonding forces between them and we say that the substance has become a liquid. Considerably more energy has to be given to the molecules before they are able to overcome the attraction which is exerted on molecules in the surface of a liquid. When the average energy of the molecules is sufficient for this to happen, the liquid is said to be boiling. Of course, some molecules will have greater than the average energy and so will be able to escape long before the bulk of the liquid boils. The gradual loss of molecules in this way is called evaporation.

Problems 4.5

1. From table 7, which metal would you select to use in the manu-facture of electric lamps where the metal must be sealed into glass?
2. A bi-metal strip consists of a length of phosphor bronze riveted longitudinally to a length of iron. When it is heated the strip is found to bend. Which metal would be on the inside of the curve?
3. Account for the large coefficient of linear expansion of solder. What would you expect to be the coefficient of linear expansion of tin from the figures quoted in the table?
4. A piece of iron rod is 1 m. long. How long should a piece of copper rod be if it is to expand by the same amount as the iron rod?
5. A rod is 100 cm. long and consists of two sections, one of copper and one of iron. How long should they be if the coefficient of linear expansion of the rod must be 15 × 10⁻⁶ deg.⁻¹ C.?

Chapter 5
Electricity: the unseen force

It was suggested in chapter 4 that just as there is a relationship between mechanical energy and heat energy, so there is a very similar connection between electrical energy and heat. If this is so we should find it possible to explain electricity in terms of molecular motion very much as we described heat. It is, in fact, to the structure of the atom which we must look to discover the nature of electricity.

In chapter 3 some account was given of the atomic structure of matter. It was explained that the nucleus of an atom could contain protons and neutrons, and that the charge of the nucleus was balanced by the sum of the charges on the orbiting electrons. These electrons orbit in definite paths which can be considered as layers or shells around the nucleus. In the case of hydrogen (1 electron) and helium (2 electrons), the electrons orbit in the innermost shell, but this shell cannot contain more than 2 electrons. The next element, with 3 electrons, is lithium (fig. 6), which has a full innermost shell and 1 electron in a second shell. This second shell needs 8 electrons before it is full. A third shell (maximum 18 electrons) is then necessary and later a fourth (32 electrons).

The importance of this theory is that the distribution of the electrons enables us to explain the phenomena of electricity. More than this, the electrons and their distribution are the 'fingerprints' of the elements, and there are many examples of the properties of elements being predicted before the element itself had even been isolated. For example, metals are characterized by their shiny lustre, their ability to be drawn into wires and beaten into sheets, and (of importance here) their ability to conduct heat and electricity. With only a few exceptions the good conductors of electricity are metals, and metals have at least one full electron shell and a few (not more than four) electrons in an incomplete outer shell. For instance, copper, silver and gold all have one electron in their outermost shell, and in each case this electron can be readily detached because it orbits furthest from the nucleus; all these metals are excellent conductors of electricity. Iron and zinc are poorer conductors: they each have two electrons in their outermost shells. Lead, an even poorer conductor, has four outer electrons. The important thing is the ease with which the outer electrons can be detached.

Electricity consists of the movement of electrons in the outermost shell in an ordered fashion due to the presence of some electric force. Each electron carries a charge, so that an electric current is the movement of this charge and could be measured as the number of electrons passing a point per second. This would be a very large number for quite small currents; for instance, a current of 1 ampere is a flow of $6 \cdot 25 \times 10^{19}$ electrons per second. It is for this reason that currents are measured in amperes (A.) and milliamperes ($\frac{1}{1000}$ ampere).

The effects of a current

We have already used an electric heater in an experiment in chapter 4, so we have seen that one effect of an electric current is to produce heat. Electric fires, cookers and kettles all depend on this characteristic.

Another effect of a current is to produce chemical changes. The composition of water, for example, can be easily demonstrated by passing a current through water to which has been added a trace of acid so that it will conduct the current better. At the point where the electrons pass into the water (this is termed the negative pole or cathode) hydrogen gas is formed. Similarly, oxygen is formed where the electrons leave the water. The apparatus shown in fig. 11 can be used to demonstrate this.

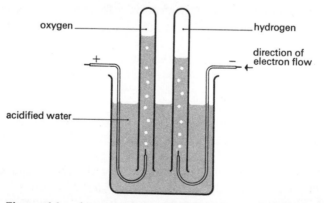

Figure 11. Apparatus to show the decomposition of water by an electrical current.

The two long tubes in the figure are first filled with water and inverted into the beaker. Current is conveyed to the water through insulated wires from near the ends of which the insulation has been removed. Carry out the experiment, and by measuring the height of gas in each tube verify the proportions of the gases in water. How could the nature of the gases be demonstrated? Why is it that the length of one column is not exactly twice the length of the other one? Why is it that a direct voltage has been used and not the alternating mains voltage?

It is often assumed that current flows from the positive terminal of a battery to the negative terminal, whereas the opposite is really true. Due to the chemical reactions which take place in a battery, surplus electrons are available at the negative terminal and there is a deficiency of electrons at the positive terminal; being deficient of negatively charged electrons, we can therefore regard it as being positively charged. In fact it is because of its positive charge that the positive terminal is able to attract electrons round through some electrical circuit from the negative terminal.

Other examples of the chemical effect of a current are to be seen in electroplating and electroforming. Electroplating is carried out to protect metal surfaces from rust or corrosion, or because the plated surface has a pleasing appearance.

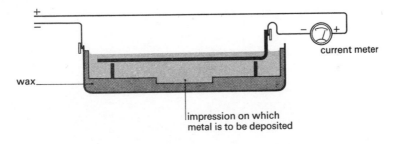

Figure 12. A simple apparatus for electroforming.

Fig. 12 shows a possible arrangement to carry out electroforming. A copper can contains some wax and also has a wax coating on the inside. The wax bears the impression of the item to be formed, perhaps a coin or other small object. The surface of the wax is dusted with graphite (a form of carbon and one of the few good non-metallic conductors of electricity). Care is taken to ensure that a graphite track is laid from the terminal on the side of the can to the impression in the wax, and a copper plate is held above it by small insulators. Copper may then be replaced from the plate into the solution as deposition continues. Copper sulphate solution is next poured carefully into the can and current passed through the apparatus as shown in the figure. Carry out the experiment, taking care to observe the correct polarity and to measure the current flowing.

What would be the result if the polarity were to be reversed? To cover an area the size of a small coin with metal the current should not exceed about 50 milliamperes, so that it will be several hours before a worthwhile deposit has been formed. After about 24 hours the shape impressed into the wax will have been reproduced in metal.

At the end of the experiment remove and weigh all the copper which has been deposited on the wax. It will then be possible to relate the mass of metal formed to the total number of electrons which passed through the copper sulphate solution. If possible also weigh the copper plate, both at the start of the experiment and at the end. Are these results more reliable than those obtained from the deposited metal? Give reasons for your answer.

The charge which is carried by the electrons through the solution is measured in coulombs. One coulomb is said to have passed when 1 ampere flows for 1 second. Since a coulomb is carried by a fixed number of electrons, $\frac{1}{10}$ ampere flowing for 10 seconds will also carry 1 coulomb. Thus charge = current × time.

In a typical experiment a constant current of 25 mA. (milliamperes) was maintained for 24 hours.

The charge transferred was therefore

$$\frac{25}{1000} \times 24 \times 3600$$

$$= 2160 \text{ coulombs.}$$

In this time the measured mass of copper deposited was 0·692 g. Thus 0·692 g. of copper were deposited by 2160 coulombs, or $\frac{0·692}{2160}$ g. per coulomb. This result of 32×10^{-8} kilograms/coulomb is the *electrochemical equivalent* of copper. It can be used to calculate the time taken to deposit a known mass of copper, but it should be noted that if the current is too high a useless soft spongy deposit will be produced.

Another important effect of a current is its magnetic effect. Electromagnets, current meters and loudspeakers depend on the fact that a conductor carrying a current can behave like a magnet, as the following experiment will show. A nickel-iron cell and suitable resistance wire[1] can be used to provide a current of about 5 amperes. In order to avoid discharging the battery too heavily this current should only be allowed to flow for a few moments.

Figure 13.   To demonstrate the magnetic effect of a current.

The wire which carries the current should pass immediately above a small compass as shown in fig. 13. What is the effect on the compass needle when the wire runs (*a*) from east to west, and (*b*) from north to south? In each case, what is the effect of (i) passing the wire beneath the compass instead of above it, and (ii) reversing the direction of the current?

From this experiment it can be seen that when a current passes through a wire, the wire acts rather like a magnet, and there is a magnetic field associated with it. The experiment also shows that the field is not very strong, for the current used, 5 amperes, is quite large. It should be noticed that with an iron magnet, unlike an electric conductor, the lines of force in the magnetic field run from the north pole of the magnet to the south pole. (A line of force can be defined as the path that a lone north pole would take were it free to move.) With a straight wire which carries a current there are no poles, the lines of force are closed, and they do not terminate at a pole (fig. 14).

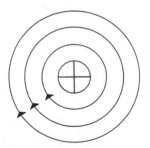

Figure 14.   The lines of magnetic force around a straight wire.

[1]Resistors will be discussed later in this chapter. If necessary this experiment may be carried out after reading the remainder of chapter 5.

In the figure the current is passing into the diagram from above the page. This results in the lines of force acting clockwise as shown. If the direction of the current is reversed, the direction of the lines of force will be reversed also.

The magnetic effect of a current is most often used when the wire is wound in a coil. The effect is also made very much greater if the coil has an iron core.

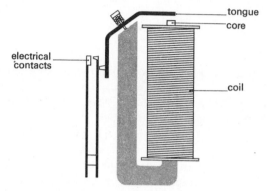

Figure 15. A relay.

Fig. 15 shows a relay, the operation of which relies on the magnetic effect of a current. When a current flows in the relay coil, the soft iron relay tongue is attracted to the iron core of the coil, and in moving closes the contacts of one or more switches. It is thus possible to switch on or off a number of quite separate devices simultaneously from the current flowing in one coil.

Problems 5.1

1. If the electrochemical equivalent of silver is 112×10^{-8} kilograms/coulomb, how long would it take to deposit 100 milligrams of silver from a silver nitrate solution at a current of 200 mA.?
2. What is the reason for the copper plate in fig. 12? What would happen if it were to be replaced by a nickel plate?
3. If a current of 25 mA. is used for electroforming a small object whose surface area is 6 cm.^{2}, calculate the current density in amperes per square metre. (Assume that no other 'waste' surface is to be plated.)
4. An industrial electroplating system uses a current density of 30 A.m.$^{-2}$ How long will it take to produce a layer of copper 10^{-3} cm. thick on a metal surface? Take the density of copper as 9 g. cm.$^{-3}$

5. List the important effects of a current, giving in each case an example of a practical application of an electrical device in which the effect is utilized.

We have already seen some of the reasons why metals are good conductors. Since the distribution of electrons is different in each substance, their conductivity will vary also. In addition, the longer a piece of wire is the more difficult it will be for the battery to set in motion the electrons along its length, so that the resistance of the wire is proportional to its length, *l*. A thick wire will present a larger number of paths for electron movement and so the resistance of the wire is inversely proportional to its cross-sectional area, *a*.

Altogether, the resistance, *R*, of a wire is given by

$$R = \frac{\rho l}{a}$$ (equation i)

where ρ is a constant depending on the material of the wire. This constant is the resistivity of the metal, and substances with low resistivities are good conductors of electricity. Some typical resistivities are given in table 8.

Table 8 Resistivities of some common substances

Substance	Ohm-cm.	Substance	Ohm-cm.
Copper	$1 \cdot 6 \times 10^{-6}$	Manganin	44×10^{-6}
Glass	4×10^{14}	Rubber	2×10^{10}
Gold	$2 \cdot 4 \times 10^{-6}$	Silver	$1 \cdot 6 \times 10^{-6}$
Iron	11×10^{-6}	Sulphur	4×10^{15}

From the table it can be seen that some substances (which are, as we should expect, metals) are very good conductors of electricity. Others (non-metals) such as glass and rubber, are very poor conductors indeed. Such materials are called insulators, and are employed where their insulating property can be put to good use.

There are also other substances (such as manganin, a metal alloy), which although good conductors are not as good as copper or silver.

Manganin is an alloy of copper, manganese and nickel and is used where it is intended to introduce small controlled amounts of resistance into an electrical circuit. One application of a 'resistance wire' of this kind is in the element of an electric fire. The design of a heating element is aimed at letting a calculated current flow from the mains supply, so that a certain amount of electrical energy will be converted to heat.

You will probably have noticed that most substances are either tolerably good conductors, or else they are insulators. There seems to be very little in between these extremes. Even manganin is a very good conductor, compared with the insulators. However, there are a few substances which can be called semi-conductors. If we were to examine their atomic structure we should find very few electrons available to take part in conduction, but the presence of very small traces of impurities can modify this situation a great deal. The production of highly specialized semi-conductor devices is an important part of the modern electronics industry.

The electrical circuit

We have seen that electricity consists of a stream of moving electrons. Since these electrons come from the atoms of conductors, it is essential that for a continued flow of current to exist these electrons must be continuously replaced by the electric source of power. Therefore a flow of electric current can only be expected to take place if there is a continuous path between the terminals of the electric supply. Such a path is called an electric circuit, and will usually consist of conductors. Should the path have an extremely low resistance, so that the electric current which flows is very high, this path is said to be a short circuit.

The source of electric power may be a dry cell, similar to those which are used for electric torches. In that case, the electricity is obtained as a result of a chemical reaction which takes place when current is drawn from the cell. When the reaction is complete the electrons are no longer available and the current ceases, so such cells cannot be recharged. They are known as primary cells.

There are also secondary cells, such as the lead-acid accumulators used to provide the electricity for cars, in which the chemical reaction is reversible. When electricity flows from the cell, the reaction continues, and would eventually cease, the current flow ceasing also. However, if a current is forced to flow through the cell in the opposite direction, the reaction may be reversed so that the cell can be recharged and will be able to pass current once again. The cell therefore stores electrical energy in the form of chemical energy.

Because of this, the energy of the cell or battery of cells can be related to the quantity of electricity which that energy can supply to some electrical circuit. If 1 joule of energy is used to pass 1 coulomb of electricity, the *electromotive force* (e.m.f.) of the cell is said to be 1 *volt* (V.). Hence a 6-volt battery converts 6 joules of energy per coulomb of electricity which flows.

There are two important points to be borne in mind. First, this is only the capability of the electric supply. It does not follow that a 6-volt battery will always supply 1 coulomb of electricity whenever it is connected to a circuit. This depends on the resistance of the circuit. If, for instance, a 6-volt battery is supplying a current of 2 amperes to a circuit, then a quantity of 2 coulombs is supplied every second. If the e.m.f. of the battery remains constant at 6 volts, then it can continue to work at this rate. Eventually, the e.m.f. will fall and the rate of working will be reduced as the chemical reaction slows down.

Secondly, the rate of working can be calculated from the figures given in this example: if 6 volts is equivalent to 6 joules per coulomb, and 2 amperes are equivalent to 2 coulombs per second, then 6 volts × 2 amperes = 12 joules per second.

We have already seen that a joule is a unit of energy, so that a joule per second must be a rate of using energy or a rate of working. It must also be related, as shown in chapter 4, to a rate of supplying heat, for the energy cannot be 'used' in the sense that it is destroyed. The energy changes to another form, such as heat.

This rate of working is called the *electrical power* which is supplied to the circuit, and is measured in *watts* (W.):

Watts = Volts × Amperes

Ohm's law

It has been explained that the e.m.f. of a cell depends on the chemical reaction which can take place when current is taken from the cell. The following experiment makes use of this fact.

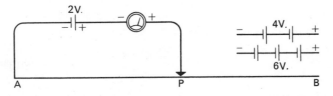

Figure 16. Apparatus for demonstrating Ohm's law.

Fig. 16 shows a 2-volt lead-acid accumulator connected by copper wires to a piece of manganin wire, AB, and a current meter. A copper wire also connects the meter to a knife-edge pointer at P. Connect the pointer momentarily to a number of points along the wire and record in each case the current flowing and the distance of the pointer from A. Take care not to connect the pointer directly to the point A, or to any point on the wire close to A, because a current might flow which would be sufficiently large to damage the meter or the cell.

From these results plot a graph of the current flowing against the reciprocal (see chapter 1) of the length AP.

Repeat the experiment using (a) two cells connected in series to give an e.m.f. of 4 volts, and (b) three cells to give 6 volts. Take particular care not to short out the battery as already explained.

The results of these experiments could be shown in a table similar to that of table 9, which has been extended to show both the length, AP, and the calculated reciprocal.

Table 9   Experimental results

Length, l, in metres	0·4	0·5	0·6	0·7	0·8	0·9	1·0
Reciprocal of l	2·5	2·0	1·7	1·4	1·25	1·1	1·0
Current in amperes							
(a) with 2 V. cell	0·50	0·40	0·33	0·29	0·25	0·22	0·20
(b) 4 V. battery	1·00	0·80	0·67	0·57	0·50	0·44	0·40
(c) 6 V. battery	1·50	1·20	1·00	0·86	0·75	0·67	0·60

These results show that for a fixed length of wire the current which flows is proportional to the e.m.f. available (take any set of three results). This is one form of Ohm's law, where this proportionality is put in the form of an equation by using a constant of proportionality, R. This is the resistance of the wire which is being used:

$$\frac{V}{I} = R \qquad \text{(equation ii)}$$

As already explained, the resistance of a wire depends on its dimensions and on the material of which it is made.

Each of the graphs you have drawn should have been a straight line. This shows that the current which flows is proportional to the reciprocal of the length of wire in the circuit (see also equation i).

Resistance is measured in ohms. Thus in table 9 it can be seen that with 1 m. of wire in use and a 2 V. cell the current was 0·20 A.; using equation (ii), the resistance of 1 m. of the wire was 10 ohms.

Now measure the diameter of the wire with a micrometer. In the experiment from which table 9 was obtained, the diameter of the wire was 0·24 mm. Thus the cross-sectional area can be obtained if the wire is assumed to be circular in section.

$$\text{Area of section} \quad = \frac{\pi d^2}{4} \text{ (this formula is derived in chapter 8)}$$

$$= \frac{22}{7 \times 4} \times (0 \cdot 024)^2 \text{ cm.}^2 \text{ (c.g.s. units)}$$

where d is the diameter of the wire.

$$\text{Therefore} \quad \text{area} = \frac{11}{14} \times \frac{576}{10^6}$$

$$= \frac{3168}{7 \times 10^6}$$

From equation (i) if $R = \dfrac{\rho l}{a}$

$$\rho = \frac{Ra}{l}$$

$$= \frac{10 \times 3168}{7 \times 10^6 \times 100}$$

$$= 45 \cdot 2 \times 10^{-6} \text{ ohm-cm.}$$

Resistivities, as in table 8, are frequently quoted in c.g.s. units of ohm-cm. In ohm-metres this result would have been $45 \cdot 2 \times 10^{-8}$ ohm-metres. This is typical of resistance wires, such as manganin and nickel-chrome alloys.

Potential drop

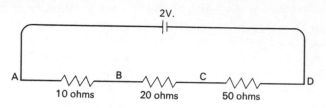

Figure 17.   A series network of resistors.

Fig. 17 shows a 2 V. cell connected across three lengths of resistance wire, known as resistors, which have been connected in series. The current has only one possible path, through each of the resistors. Let this current be I.

Then since $\dfrac{V}{I} = R$, $\quad \dfrac{2}{I} \doteq$ Total resistance $\qquad$ (equation iii)

Also the e.m.f. of the cell causes potential drops across each of these resistors. The sum of these drops, often called 'voltages', will be equal to the applied e.m.f.

Thus, $I = \dfrac{V_1}{10} = \dfrac{V_2}{20} = \dfrac{V_3}{50}$

where V_1, V_2, and V_3 are these voltages.

Also, $V_1 + V_2 + V_3 = 2$

Hence $V_1 = 10\,I$, $V_2 = 20\,I$, and $V_3 = 50\,I$.

Therefore, adding these results

$\qquad V_1 + V_2 + V_3 = (10 + 20 + 50)I = 2 \qquad$ (equation iv)

Comparing equations (iii) and (iv) we see that the total resistance is $10 + 20 + 50$ ohms, so in a simple series circuit the total resistance is equal to the sum of the separate resistances. This enables us to calculate the current which flows:

$$I = \frac{\text{applied voltage}}{\text{total resistance}}$$

$$= \frac{1}{40} \text{ A.}$$

Problems 5.2

1. Use equations (i) and (ii) to demonstrate theoretically that the current I is proportional to $1/l$ as shown in the experiment.

2. Find the current flowing when a 250 V. supply is connected to a 2 kilowatt electric fire. What will be the resistance of the fire element when it is operating?

3. Name three kinds of energy and give an example in which each of them is involved. How may energy be changed from any one of these forms to another one of them?

4. Distinguish between electrical energy and electrical power. If a loud-speaker is rated at 5 watts and operates at full rating for one hour, how many joules of electricity will have been used?

5. In fig. 17 what is the potential drop in each case between (i) A and B, (ii) A and C, and (iii) A and D?

6.

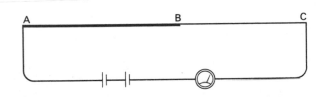

Figure 18.

Fig. 18 shows a length of resistance wire, AB, to which has been soldered a length of a different type of wire, BC, so that AC is 1 m. long. A voltmeter is connected between A and a point D on AC. The current flowing is 0·05 A. Use the results given in table 10 to construct a graph. Hence find the length AB and the resistance of each of the wires. What is the supply voltage to the wire?

Table 10

Distance AD in cm.	15	25	35	45	55	65	75
Potential drop in volts	0·15	0·25	0·35	0·80	1·6	2·4	3·0

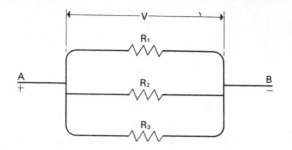

Figure 19.   A parallel network of resistors.

In discussing fig. 17 we found that the total resistance of a number of resistors in series could be found by adding the resistance of each of them.

When the resistors are connected in parallel as in fig. 19 the argument which was used before is no longer true, for the same current does not flow through each of the resistors. However, one common factor in this case is the potential drop across each resistor. This is V in the figure.

Thus, $V = I_1 R_1 = I_2 R_2 = I_3 R_3$

where I_1, I_2, and I_3 are the currents in each of the resistors. Also $I_1 + I_2 + I_3 = I$, the total current, and $V = IR$ where R is the effective resistance of the network.

From these equations we have

$$\frac{I}{V} = \frac{1}{R}$$

and $$\frac{I_1 + I_2 + I_3}{V} = \frac{I}{V} = \frac{1}{R_1} + \frac{1}{R_2} + \frac{1}{R_3}$$

Therefore, $$\frac{1}{R} = \frac{1}{R_1} + \frac{1}{R_2} + \frac{1}{R_3}$$ (equation v)

Equation (v) gives the reciprocal rule which must always be used for adding parallel combinations of resistors. For example, if the resistors are the same values as in the previous example (10, 20 and 50 ohms) the effective resistance, R, can be found.

$$\frac{1}{R} = \frac{1}{10} + \frac{1}{20} + \frac{1}{50}$$

$$= \frac{10 + 5 + 2}{100}$$

$$= \frac{17}{100}$$

Therefore $R = \frac{100}{17}$ ohms

$= 5\cdot88$ ohms

Notice here a simple check which you can use. When calculating the effective resistance of a number of resistors in parallel, the result is always lower than the lowest resistance. In this case the effective resistance, 5·88 ohms, is clearly less than the lowest resistance, 10 ohms.

Example

Four resistors, each of 1000 ohms resistance, form the sides of a square. What is the effective resistance between opposite corners of the square?

There are two current paths between opposite corners of the square, and each of them is through two resistances in series. Each path consequently has a resistance of 2000 ohms.

The effective resistance, R, is given by

$$\frac{1}{R} = \frac{1}{2000} + \frac{1}{2000}$$

Therefore $R = 1000$ ohms

The effect of temperature changes on resistance

A substance, such as a metal, which has one or more loosely bound electrons to each atom is, as we have seen, a good conductor. However, when the temperature of the metal is raised, energy is given to its atoms so that they move about more rapidly. Because the atoms are in motion an electron, under the action of an e.m.f., will now probably have other forces influencing its path through the substance, so that the effect of the e.m.f. will be somewhat less than before. The effect of heat on a good conductor is thus to cause it to conduct less, in other words to raise its resistance. For example, the element of an electric fire will have a lower resistance when it is cold than after current has commenced to flow through it, when it becomes hot.

Pass a small current from a battery through the element of a 1 kilowatt electric fire. By measuring the voltage applied to the element and the current which flows, calculate the resistance of the element. Then from a knowledge of its electric power, its resistance when hot can be found. Its hot resistance, R_t, at a temperature $t°C$. is given by

$$R_t = \frac{V^2}{W}$$

where V is the supply voltage (250 V.) and W is the power in watts (1000 W.).

Thus, in this experiment,

$$R_t = \frac{(250)^2}{1000}$$
$$= 62\cdot5 \text{ ohms}$$

It is possible to measure the temperature of the fire by using a pyrometer. In one form of this instrument the colour of a small glowing lamp filament is matched to that of the hot object by adjusting the current flowing through the lamp filament, and the temperature is read off a calibration chart provided by the instrument manufacturer.

If a pyrometer is available, you will be able to show that the temperature of the element when it is operating is probably about 1000°C. At this temperature the resistance of the element may well be about four times as great as when it is cold.

By a similar experiment it can be shown that the resistance of a conductor can be made to change by applying a pressure to it; for example, the resistance of a fine wire which is stretched will rise.

Now we will consider the effect of temperature on a material which is not a good conductor. At low temperatures there will be hardly any electrons free to take part in conduction, but as the temperature is raised the thermal energy is partly given to the electrons, so increasing the number of free electrons present. This effect would be insignificant in a good conductor which has plenty of free electrons already, but it will be much more important here, where we should expect the resistance of semiconductors and insulators to fall with an increase of temperature.

Problems 5.3

1. The resistance of a piece of copper wire is 50 ohms at 20°C. and 66 ohms at 100°C. Find the increase in resistance per ohm for a 1 deg. C. rise and hence find the resistance at 60°C. of a piece of copper wire which had 35 ohms resistance at 20°C.

2. What resistance must be placed in parallel with a 120-ohm resistor so that the effective resistance of the combination is 100 ohms?

3. Two resistors, each of 4 ohms resistance, are connected in parallel, and this combination is placed in series with a resistance of 2 ohms. Find the resistance of the combination and the power dissipated in each resistor if the network is connected to a 2 V. cell.

4. A number of lamps are rated at 24 volts, 100 mA. Show how they may be connected to the 240 V. mains so as to decorate a Christmas tree. What current will flow, and how many lamps will be needed?

5. A current meter has a resistance of 0·10 ohms and reads 1 A. full-scale. What voltage drop will there be across the meter? What current will be needed to give a full-scale deflection on the meter if 0·01 ohms are placed in parallel with it?

6. A current meter has a resistance of 25 ohms and reads 10 mA. full-scale. What resistance must be placed in parallel with it to adapt the meter to read 100 mA. full-scale?

7. What is understood by Ohm's law? Name two physical conditions which must be maintained constant in any experiment to demonstrate the law.

8. A car has two headlamps, each rated at 36 watts, and two side lamps and two rear lamps each rated at 12 watts. What are the possible currents taken from the 12 V. battery when the car's lighting is in use?

Chapter 6
Mechanical force

In chapter 2 force was defined as that which opposes or attempts to oppose either a body remaining at rest or one which is continuing to move with constant speed in a straight line. It is easy to understand that force is necessary to move a stationary object: we can appreciate that when the surface on which an object is resting is rough a very large force will be required, and even when it is smooth considerable effort may be needed to enable the object to gain speed. On the Earth there are always forces opposing the motion of a body (gravitation, friction and air resistance for example) but in space an object can continue to move at a constant speed in a straight line without it being necessary to apply any force. However, if a space craft must change direction or speed, it exerts force by using its jets, and if it must slow down, perhaps to re-enter the Earth's atmosphere, then its retrorockets must be fired. Here too a force has been used.

How then can a space craft continue to orbit around the Earth without using any force, when its path is clearly not in a straight line? The force which is necessary comes from the force of gravity and not from the space craft. In the same way, the Earth remains in orbit around the Sun, not because we steer the Earth in that direction, but because of the gravitational force of the Sun acting on the Earth.

Practical force problems are seldom simple because nearly always a number of forces are involved. The smaller this number is the more simple the problem becomes. In this chapter we shall learn by examining problems where there are only a few forces. To see how forces complicate a problem, consider a car being driven downhill. One obvious force present is the pull of the engine, but there are also frictional forces between each tyre and the road, there is the pull of gravity on the car and the resistance of the wind at the time. The following experiment will give you some experience with multiple force problems which are somewhat simpler than this.

Triangle of forces

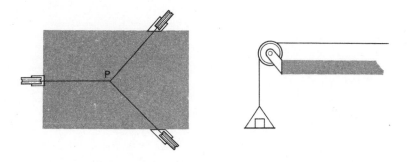

Figure 20.   Apparatus for measuring the forces at a point.

Fig. 20 shows a plan view of a small table around which three pulleys are placed. A detailed view of one of these is also shown in the figure. A string passes over each pulley and carries a scale pan and weights. The three strings are joined at a point, P. Assemble the apparatus with suitable weights in the pans, so that P is conveniently placed near the centre of the table. Now place a piece of paper on the table under the strings so that the position of P and the directions of the strings can be marked on it; the lines on the paper now represent the directions of the strings, each of which is kept taut by a force along its length. This force is due to the weight of the attached scale pan and its contents. Since this force pulls away from the point P, it is usual to put an arrowhead in this direction on each of the lines from P. We can then mark the paper beside each arrowhead with the force in the string to which it corresponds.

The purpose of this experiment is to examine the forces which act on P when this point is at rest. P is then said to be *in equilibrium* under the forces. Repeat the experiment a number of times with different loads, and using different pieces of paper to record your results. Fig. 21 shows a typical set of readings which we will use to illustrate an important principle. Notice that by marking the angles as in the figure it is easy to reproduce the drawing later on.

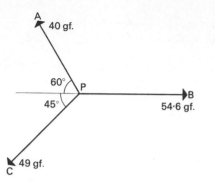

Figure 21.   Diagram to show the forces at a point.

In the figure the point of application of the forces is the point P, and the directions of the forces are shown by the arrowheads. The magnitude (size) of the forces can be shown merely by placing figures beside them, but alternatively we could draw the lines to some scale so that in each case the distance from P to the arrowhead is proportional to the magnitude of the force. This has been done in fig. 21.

An interesting conclusion can be deduced from this way of representing a force. Take any of the forces acting on P, for instance AP, and represent it in the way just described. Then select the other forces in order in a clockwise direction, drawing the second, in the direction shown in fig. 21, so that its tail touches the arrowhead of the first. Similarly, the third is drawn in the same direction as before, but so that its tail touches the arrowhead of the second line. This is shown in fig. 22.

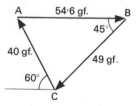

Figure 22.   Triangle of forces.

From the figure it can be seen that the arrowhead of the third force chosen touches the tail of the first one, so that the three forces form a triangle. This will always happen when three forces are in equilibrium, but if the three forces are not in equilibrium then the length of the line which must be drawn to close the figure represents the force which is necessary to bring the forces to equilibrium; that is, to bring to rest the point, such as P, at which the forces are acting.

Verify that the results you have obtained can also be used to give closed triangles.

How may the rule be modified if there are more than three forces? Investigate this using four or five strings and pulleys instead of three.

Problems 6.1

1. Three light ropes are tied at a common point, and three men, A, B, and C, each pull horizontally on one of the ropes. If A pulls on one rope with a force of 40 kgf. and B pulls on a second rope at right angles to A with a force of 50 kgf., find the force C must exert on the third rope to prevent the knot where the ropes join from moving. Find also the direction in which he must pull.

2. Two light ropes are fixed to a stake in the ground and a man pulls horizontally on each with a force of 40 kgf. If the ropes are at an angle of 45 degrees to each other, find the force which a third rope, also tied to the stake, must transmit, so that there shall be no tendency to move the stake. In the absence of this third rope, how is it that the stake may remain in the ground?

3. A weight of 100 gf. is suspended by a string (whose length is unimportant) which is in turn joined by a small loop to a second string so that it can slide along it. This string is fixed to two points 10 cm. apart. If this string is 25 cm. long find the tension in each part of the upper string.

4. A weight of 1 kgf. is supported by two rods each at 45 degrees to the horizontal. What is the force in each rod?

5. A weight of 1 kgf. is supported by a rod at 45 degrees to the horizontal below the weight and by a string also at 45° immediately above this rod. What are the forces in the string and in the rod?

Questions 1 to 3 described situations in which forces were transmitted along ropes or strings. If it is possible to ignore the weight of each of these ropes then they can always be assumed to be straight and so long as the rope is taut the force on one end will also be exerted at the other end, *but in the opposite direction*. Thus, if two men pull on a rope against each other, then the rope will be taut, with the force in the rope along its length and always in that direction which opposes the pull of each of the men. This can easily be demonstrated by cutting the rope when, if the men continue to pull, they will fall away from each other, since there is now no longer any tension acting in opposite directions at the ends of the rope.

For this reason when a diagram is drawn in which there is a taut rope, the arrows on the rope, representing the forces in it, should point away from the ends of the rope.

We have said that the rope is in tension. Tension in any rope or rod is shown in this way. In question 4, a force (actually a weight force) acting downwards was opposed by forces in two rods which acted upwards along the lengths of the rods to prevent the weight falling. At the far ends of the rods, which rested perhaps on a flat surface, the forces transmitted through the rods must be acting downwards. Thus, in this case, the arrows which are drawn on the diagram point towards the ends of the rods, showing that the forces which the rods transmit are directed outwards to oppose the *compression* of the rod.

A rod, being rigid, can be either in tension or in compression, but a rope is only rigid when in tension, so it cannot carry compressive forces. For instance, in question 4 the rods could not have been replaced by ropes, unless the weight was hung from them. However, if rods are used, the weight could be supported by the rods beneath it, or by being hung from the rods. In such cases you are left to decide which the question intends. What difference does this make to the result of the calculation?

Spring balances are used to measure the tensile and compressive forces. They depend on calibrating the extension of a spring when a load is applied to it.

Action and reaction

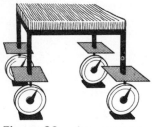

Figure 23.   Apparatus to measure the reactions at the supports.

Fig. 23 shows a small four-legged stool with each leg supported on a spring balance. Find a suitable stool, weigh it and then construct an arrangement like this, so that the readings of the spring balances can be seen and recorded. Add certain known weights to the stool, placing them on different parts of the top of the stool. What can you deduce about the total weight, including the stool, and the readings of the spring balances? Do all the spring balances show an identical reading when a load is moved from one part of the top of the stool to another or does the reading of each balance depend on the position of the load on the stool?

An experiment like this helps us to understand a little more about question 4. If in this question the weight was supported by the rods beneath it, the rods were under compression, and so were exerting a force on the surface on which they were standing. (Had the weight been hanging from them, they would have been in tension, although the magnitude of the forces would have been unaltered.) Similarly, when you are standing or sitting, your weight is acting on the surface which supports you. Since weight is a force we should expect this force to cause motion. Then why do you not sink into the ground on which you are standing? It can only be because the ground exerts a force upwards on you, which is equal to the force you exert on the ground. It cannot be less than this or you would sink, and it cannot be greater, or you would rise. Neither is it possible to 'catch the ground unawares' by suddenly moving and expecting this upwards force to lift the ground from where you stood.

Solid objects have the ability to support other objects in this way. The opposing force which they provide is called a reaction, for it is equal and in the opposite direction to the action of the force upon it. There is a practical limit to the size of the reaction which a surface can supply, since if the load is too great the surface will be deformed by the load.

In the experiment, the four spring balances' readings showed the four reactions between the legs and the surface on which they were supported. The sum of the reactions must be equal to the total load on the balances, but you will have found that these reactions were not necessarily all equal.

Moments

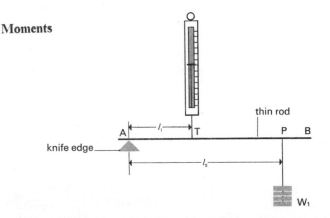

Figure 24. Apparatus to demonstrate the law of moments.

Fig. 24 shows a light rod, AB. A weight, W_1, is hung from a point P on the rod so that P is a distance, l_2, from the knife edge on which the rod rests. The rod is prevented from turning by a cord which is attached to a spring balance. The balance is used to measure the tension in the cord, the distance of the cord from the knife edge being l_1. Let the tension in the cord be T.

Now the weight, W_1, tends to make the rod turn clockwise. It is prevented from doing so by the force, T, which were it to exist unaltered on its own, would tend to make the rod turn anticlockwise.

The turning effect of a force is found to be proportional to the perpendicular distance from the line of action of the force to the point about which the rod turns. This might be stated in everyday terms as 'the longer the lever, the greater the leverage'.

Thus the turning effect in a clockwise direction, often called the *clockwise moment*, is $W_1 \times l_2$. Similarly, the *anticlockwise moment* is $T \times l_1$. Then, since the rod does not turn, these moments can be equated so that $W_1 l_2 = T\, l_1$.

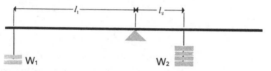

Figure 25.   Diagram to show the forces acting on a rod in equilibrium.

Fig. 25 shows two weights which have been hung from opposite sides of a metre rule pivoted about its centre.

Set up the apparatus, with W_1 not equal to W_2, and record values of l_1 and l_2 when the rule balances horizontally. Some typical results are shown in table 11.

Table 11

W_1 g.	l_1 cm.	W_2 g.	l_2 cm.
40	20	60	13·3
40	15	60	10·0
40	30	60	20·0
30	50	70	21·4
30	40	70	17·1

These results can be used to show that the clockwise and anticlockwise moments are equal when the rule is balanced.

In each case,
$$W_1\, l_1 = W_2\, l_2.$$

This example is relatively simple because there is no turning moment due to the weight of the rule, since this weight acts directly above the pivot.

Fig. 26 shows a diagram of an experimental arrangement in which weights are hung from a metre rule supported on two spring balances.

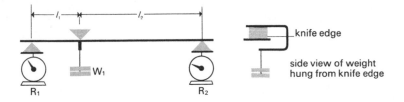

Figure 26.   Apparatus for experiments on moments.

First set up the metre rule and spring balances without using any other load. The rule should be supported on knife edges as shown in the figure. These knife edges should be at equal distances (e.g. 5 cm.) from the ends of the rule. Observe that the spring balances then have equal readings. Now add a weight, W_1, of 500 g. to some point on the rod. This can be supported by a light framework as shown in the small diagram. Move this along the rule until the readings on the balances are again equal. Check that this occurs when W_1 is midway between the ends of the rule. From this we can also deduce that the weight of the metre rule must act midway along its length.

Now move W_1 to some other point on the rule and record the reactions R_1 and R_2, which are indicated by the balances. Repeat this with W_1 at a number of other points on the rule. From these readings it is possible to demonstrate a method which will enable us to calculate the reactions if the weight and position of W_1 are known. We can, of course, check our results because in this case we can read the reactions on the spring balances. However, if the rule were balanced between knife edges on a flat surface without the spring balances this would not be possible. The experiment will, therefore, give us a method for use in such circumstances.

To illustrate this experiment here, we shall use a set of typical results (table 12), but you should repeat the following work with the results you have just obtained.

Table 12

Weight of metre rule 40 gf., $W_1 = 500$ gf.
Knife edges are placed 5 cm. from each end of rule.

R_1 gf.	R_2 gf.	l_1 cm.	l_2 cm.
464·5	75·5	10	80
		20	70
		30	60
		40	50
		45	45

The first point to note is that since the rule is at rest, the sum of the forces acting on it must be zero. Alternatively, this idea can be expressed by saying that there must be no *resultant force* on the rule. We see in the table that the sum of the weights acting downwards is equal to the sum of the reactions, acting upwards, in every case.

Secondly, the rule does not tend to tip about either of the knife edges on which it is supported. Now, using the principle of moments, in which for a rod at rest clockwise and anticlockwise moments are equal, it is possible to take moments about some convenient point on the rule. In practice, the most useful point is where one of the reactions acts, because we know that the moment of that reaction about its own line of action will be zero. This simplifies the calculations. For example, using the first line of table 12, and taking moments about the line of action of R_1,

$$W_1\, l_1 + W_2\, l_3 = R_2\, (l_1 + l_2)$$

where W_2 is the weight of the rule and l_3 is the distance from its midpoint to the line of action of R_1.

Therefore, $5000 + 1800 = 90\ R_2$

or, $\qquad\qquad\qquad R_2 = 75\frac{5}{9}$ g.

Again, taking moments about the line of action of R_2,

$$W_1\ l_2 + W_2\ l_3 = R_1\ (l_1 + l_2)*$$
$$40{,}000 + 1800 = 90\ R_1$$
$$R_1 = 464\tfrac{4}{9}\ \text{gf}.$$

These results compare well with the measured values of R_1 and R_2.

Problems 6.2

1. In table 12 the values of R_1 and R_2 are only given in the first set of results. What are these values in the remaining cases?
2. Repeat the experiment associated with fig. 26, but using an additional weight, W_2. If W_2 is 400 gf., find the reactions when it is placed 10 cm. from the line of action of R_1 with W_1 (500 gf.) placed 20 cm. from R_1.
3. An iron bar 80 cm. long is used to lift 5 kgf. by pivoting it 15 cm. from one end of the bar. What force will be required if this force is applied 5 cm. from the other end of the bar? How is this force altered when your calculations make allowance for the weight of the bar?
4. A light triangular framework of three rods measuring 30 cm., 40 cm. and 50 cm. is hung by one of its corners, and weights are then hung from the other two corners so that the side joining them is horizontal. Calculate the greater of these weights if in each case the lesser weight is 1 kgf. (A scale drawing may be useful.)
5. A light horizontal beam 1 metre long is free to turn about a point 5 cm. from one end and carries 1 kgf. 5 cm. from the other end. A light cord is fixed to the beam 50 cm. from the pivot and its other end is attached to a point 50 cm. directly above the pivot. Find the tension in this cord.

In problem 3 an iron bar was used as a lever. Such problems can usually be solved by taking moments about some convenient point. The art of solving this kind of problem lies in the choice of the point. It is frequently useful to take moments about some point at which the object pivots, particularly where the reaction at this point is unknown and need not be found; the pivot is also known as the *fulcrum* of the lever, whilst the ratio of the useful weight lifted to the applied effort is called the lever's mechanical advantage.

* l_3 can only be used in this equation if the rod is placed symmetrically. If it is not, a new length, l_4, must be used.

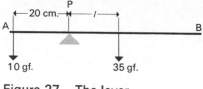

Figure 27.   The lever.

In fig. 27 the unknown length, l, must be found for the light rod, AB, to balance horizontally.

Taking moments about P,

$$10 \times 20 = 35l$$

Therefore, $$l = \frac{200}{35}$$

$$= 5\tfrac{5}{7} \text{ cm.}$$

Alternatively, taking moments about A,

$$35 (20 + l) = 20R$$

where R is the reaction at the point P.

Also, equating forces on the rod upwards and downwards,

$$R = 45 \text{ gf.}$$

Therefore, $35 (20 + l) = 20 \times 45$

or $$700 + 35l = 900$$

so that $$l = \frac{200}{35}$$

$$= 5\tfrac{5}{7} \text{ cm.}$$

In this case the second method was longer than the first, although on occasions taking moments about some point other than the pivot can be very useful. For instance, in problem 5 there is a reaction at the pivot. If we take moments about the point where the cord is fastened to the beam, the clockwise moment will be 40 kgf.cm. This must therefore also be the value of the moment of the reaction of the pivot about this force. Since this reaction is 50 cm. from the cord there must be a reaction vertically downwards of 0·8 kgf.

If we now take moments about the upper end of the cord so that again the tension of the cord is not taken into account we have clockwise 90 kgf.cm. and hence the anticlockwise reaction at the pivot Q will be given by

$$50Q = 90$$

Therefore $Q = 1 \cdot 8$ kgf.

Hence it seems as though there are two different results which can be calculated for this reaction. In fact, the reaction has two *components*, R acting vertically and Q acting horizontally. We did not discover Q in the first case because it had no moment about the lower end of the rod. Similarly, the line of action of R passes through the upper end of the cord and so has zero moment in the second part of the problem.

The total reaction at the pivot will be due to both of these components as shown in fig. 28.

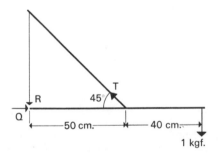

Figure 28. Components of forces acting on a pivoted rod.

Using the triangle of forces we can find one force which will exactly balance Q and R. However, Q and R are not separate forces, they are the horizontal and vertical components of one force, the reaction at the pivot. This force must be equal and opposite to the opposing force found from the triangle of forces. Thus we see that the triangle of forces can also be used to find the resultant of two components, except that in this case the direction of the arrowhead on the third side of the triangle must be reversed.

Problems 6.3

1. In fig. 28 calculate the reaction of which Q and R are components. At what angle to the horizontal does it act?

2. In the previous example, reposition the string so that its lower end is connected to the same point on the rod as the weight. Use a scale drawing to find the tension in the string and the reaction at the pivot.

3. A light rod, 1 metre long, is used as a lever with its fulcrum 20 cm. from one end. What effort applied at the longer end is needed to lift 4 kgf.? Also find the mechanical advantage of the lever. How would the results be modified if the rod was a length of metal piping weighing 600 gf.? How heavy would the rod need to be before no effort was needed to lift the load?

4. Fig. 29 shows a section through a light roof structure made from three rods, AB, AC and BC. If it carries a load of 50 kgf. at A, find the forces in the rods AB and AC and so find the force in the rod BC and the reactions at B and C. Which rods are being compressed and which are in tension?

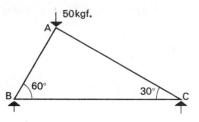

Figure 29.

5. A force of 200 gf. must be applied to the opposite faces of a piece of coal by a pair of coal tongs. If the tongs are gripped 7 cm. from the hinge and the distance from the hinge to the load (the coal) is 25 cm., find (a) the effort needed on each limb of the tongs, and (b) the mechanical advantage of the tongs. What is unusual about this result? Name some other lever with a mechanical advantage similar to this.

Chapter 7
Mathematical aids to force problems

It is important to read chapter 6 before commencing this chapter. Here we shall be examining some mathematical tools, particularly those which can be of assistance in solving the kind of problem which we met in chapter 6; much of the work we are now going to study is therefore concerned with the properties of angles.

Angles

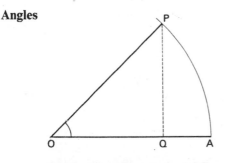

Figure 30.   The angle AOP.

In fig. 30 the line OA is fixed, and a second line, OP (equal in length to OA), rotates about the point O. Therefore as P moves, its path is that of the circumference of a circle. A perpendicular is then dropped from P on to OA at Q. A number of important properties of the angle at O can be stated in terms of the lengths OP, OQ and PQ.

Consider first the lengths OP and OQ. When P is almost at A so that the angle at O is very small, OP and OQ are nearly equal. When P is immediately above O, so that the angle is a right angle, OQ is zero. As P moves from A round the circumference of the circle, Q moves from A towards O.

The ratio OQ/OP is the *cosine* of the angle at O, and as O increases from 0° to 90°, the cosine of the angle decreases from 1 to 0.

Construct the figure with a number of points (P_{10}, P_{20}, etc.) at intervals of 10° from A. Hence measure OP and OQ and so evaluate the cosines of the angles 10°, 20°, etc. to 90°.

Since cosines are ratios of two lengths, it follows that if one of these lengths be changed, so that the other changes also, in the way just described, the cosine is unaltered so long as the angle between the lines remains the same, no matter how long the arm OP might be. Thus, if either OP or OR is known, the unknown length can be calculated from the cosine of the angle between them.

$$OQ = OP \cos P\hat{O}Q$$

and $\quad OP = OQ/\cos P\hat{O}Q$

Tables of the cosines of angles between 0° and 90° are commonly available and should be used to check the results you have just obtained. They may also be used in the examples in the remainder of this chapter.

The cosines of 0°, 30°, 45°, 60° and 90° should be memorized. They can be found easily if it is remembered that the cosine of an angle is the ratio of the adjacent side to the hypotenuse of a right-angled triangle. Clearly, cos 0° = 1, and cos 90° = 0, but to find the cosine of 30° or 60° consider an equilateral triangle as shown in fig. 31.

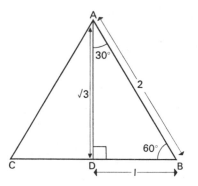

Figure 31.   The angles of an equilateral triangle.

If the sides of the triangle are each of length two units, then DB is one unit, if D is the midpoint of BC. Also, AD is $\sqrt{3}$ units by Pythagoras' theorem. Now consider the triangle ABD. In this, cos 30° = AD/AB =

$\sqrt{3}/2$. Similarly, $\cos 60° = DB/AB = 1/2$. Then by considering a triangle whose angles are 45°, 45°, and 90° it can be seen that $\cos 45° = \sqrt{2}/2$.

In chapter 6 it was stated that the force acting in a given direction could be resolved into components acting vertically and horizontally. This technique can often be used to find the value of an unknown force. An example of this kind is illustrated in fig. 32 in which a light rod is pivoted at one end. The other end carries a load of 1 kgf. and is attached by a light cord to a point above the pivot as shown in the figure. The tension in the cord and the thrust in the rod must be found.

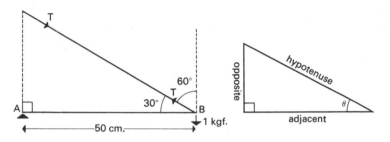

Figure 32.   The resolved part of a force.

Let the tension in the cord be T. Now there will be a force in the rod, AB, which acts along its length. If we consider the vertical components of the forces at B, this force in AB cannot enter into our calculations, so 1 kgf. is the force downwards, and the component of the force T, T cos 60°, is the force upwards.

Thus   1 kgf. $= \text{T} \cos 60°$

$= \dfrac{\text{T}}{2}$

or $\text{T} = 2$ kgf.

Similarly, if we consider only the horizontal components of forces at B, the two forces acting are (i) the horizontal component of T, which is T cos 30°, and (ii) the horizontal thrust, F, in the rod.

$\text{F} = \text{T} \cos 30°$

$\text{F} = \dfrac{\sqrt{3}}{2} \text{T}$

$= 0{\cdot}866 \text{ T}$

Problems 7.1

1. Prove that cos 45° = $\sqrt{2}/2$ exactly.

2. Redraw fig. 32 with the cord at an angle of 45° to the rod. Hence find the value of the new tension in the cord and the thrust in the rod.

3. A uniform rod, AB, weighs 2 kgf. and is 10 cm. long. Its ends are connected by two equal light cords 50 cm. long to a point P above it. What is the tension in the cords?

4. Find the tension in the cord in the problem of fig. 32 by taking moments about the point A in the figure. If necessary, make a scale drawing.

5. A triangle, ABC, has AB equal to 20 cm. and BC equal to 10 cm. If the angle $A\hat{C}B$ is a right-angle, and D is a point on AB so that CD is perpendicular to AB, find the lengths AD and CD.

The ratio OQ/OP in fig. 30 is the cosine of the angle $P\hat{O}Q$. Another useful ratio is QP/OP. This is the *sine* of the angle $P\hat{O}Q$.

From fig. 31 we have

$$\frac{DB}{AB} = \sin 30°$$

Hence $\sin 30° = \frac{1}{2}$

Similarly we can find the sines of 0°, 45°, 60°, and 90°. It is interesting to note that sin 30° = cos 60°. Generally, it is true that the sine of any angle between 0° and 90° is equal to the cosine of that angle subtracted from 90°.

Then in fig. 32 the vertical forces acting at B are 1 kgf. downwards and T sin 30° upwards.

Hence T sin 30° = 1 kgf.

so that by this method also we find

$$T = 2 \text{ kgf.}$$

Resolution of forces

If a force acts at some angle to a convenient direction, such as the horizontal line in fig. 33, then it is possible to bring to rest a particle acted on by this force by applying two other forces to it. In the figure, OP can be regarded as being in equilibrium with two forces in the directions YO and XO, so that the three forces, taken in order, form a closed triangle.

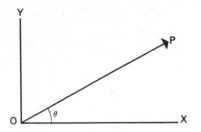

Figure 33. Vertical and horizontal components.

Hence if OP is in equilibrium with these forces, OP can be replaced by two equal opposite forces in the directions OY and OX. These forces are said to be the *vertical* and *horizontal components* of OP, and OP is said to be *resolved* into its components. This technique is exactly what we found in chapter 6 when we examined the two components of the reaction in problem 6.2.5.

Friction

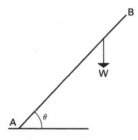

Figure 34. The inclined plane.

Fig. 34 shows an inclined plane on which an object of weight, W, is able to remain at rest. This is only possible because the plane is not smooth and there is thus friction between the object and the plane. The force of friction prevents the object from sliding down the plane. Therefore it must act upwards along the plane. It follows from the arguments put forward in chapter 6 that two forces can only be in equilibrium when they are equal in magnitude and act in exactly opposite directions. This is not the case here, so there must be a third force acting on the object. This force is the reaction of the surface due to the weight of the object. Now a surface is only able to resist objects which press against it, so that the reaction of the surface must be acting at right angles to the surface.

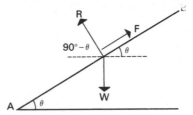

Figure 35. The forces acting on a body which is in
equilibrium on an inclined plane.

Fig. 35 shows all the forces which are acting on the object. Forces which pull *horizontally* on the object must be equal to zero because the object does not move.

Thus, resolving horizontally

$$R \cos (90 - \theta) = F \cos \theta$$

or $\quad R \sin \theta \qquad = F \cos \theta \qquad\qquad$ (equation vi)

Similarly, examining the forces which act vertically on the object, that is resolving vertically

$$R \sin (90 - \theta) + F \sin \theta = W$$

or $\quad R \cos \theta \qquad + F \sin \theta = W \qquad\qquad$ (equation vii)

These equations can be solved if W and θ are known. For instance, if $W = 1$ kgf. and $\theta = 30°$, from equation (vi)

$$\frac{R}{2} = \frac{\sqrt{3}\,F}{2}$$

or $\quad R = \sqrt{3}\,F$

From equation (vii)

$$\frac{\sqrt{3}\,R}{2} + \frac{F}{2} = 1$$

or $\quad \sqrt{3}\,R + F = 2$

Substituting for $R\ (= \sqrt{3}\,F)$

$$4\,F = 2$$

or $$F = 0\cdot5 \text{ kgf.}$$

Similarly $$R = 0\cdot866 \text{ kgf.}$$

Looking again at fig. 30, there is one more interesting ratio. It is PQ/OQ. This is the *tangent* of the angle POQ.

By the same methods as before the tangents of certain angles can easily be found. Of course, if we are limited to the use of these few angles, the power of this particular mathematical tool will be restricted. However, tables of sines, cosines and tangents can readily be obtained and it will be assumed that such tables are available for use with the problems in the remainder of this book.

If, in fig. 33, the horizontal component only of a force OX is known, and the vertical component OY must be found, then

$$\frac{OY}{OX} = \tan\theta$$

or $$OY = OX\tan\theta$$

Example

The shorter sides of a right-angled triangle are 11 cm. and 60 cm. What are the other angles of the triangle?

Let the smaller angle be θ

Then $$\tan\theta = \frac{11}{60}$$

$$= 0\cdot1833$$

From tables $\theta = 10°\ 20'$

How can the other angle be found?

Problems 7.2

1. Complete table 13 by calculations (such as those based on right-angled triangles suggested earlier in the chapter). These results should be committed to memory.

Table 13 Trigonometrical functions

Function	angle				
	0°	30°	45°	60°	90°
sine					
cosine					
tangent					

2. The elevation of the top of a television transmitting aerial mast is 11° 20′ at a distance of 500 metres from its base. How high is the tower?

3. A tunnel must be bored horizontally from the foot of a mountain until a point immediately below the peak. The elevation of the peak from the mouth of the tunnel is 5° 44′ and from a point 2 km. farther from the peak at the same horizontal level is 4° 46′. How long will the tunnel be? Also find the height of the mountain.

4. Six metal bars of equal length are laid end to end to form a regular hexagon. Find (i) the shortest, and (ii) the longest distance between the bars on the opposite sides of the hexagon, passing through its centre. Note that the internal angles of a hexagon are 120°.

5. A ladder 5 metres long is used to reach a window, the bottom of which is 4 metres above the ground. At what angle does the ladder slope? If the ladder is now moved until it slopes at 65° to the horizontal, to what height will it reach?

Centre of gravity

In very many problems in which there are forces acting on an object, one of these forces is that of gravity, which gives the object what we know as weight. It is quite simple to deal with this so long as we know at what point this force is acting. In the previous examples in this chapter and in chapter 6, weight forces have been shown acting on strings or light rods. In those circumstances the point at which the weight acted was quite obvious, but is it possible to solve problems in which we are dealing with a body whose weight is not concentrated at one point? One way of doing this is to find some point, not necessarily in the body, at which the weight could be assumed to act as regards conditions external to the body. This point is the *centre of gravity* of the body.

In chapter 6 the weight of a metre rule was assumed to act midway along its length. Verify this for a heavy uniform plank using the same method (see fig. 26). By taking moments about each support in turn, find the position of the centre of gravity of the plank when it is (i) lying flat, and (ii) standing on edge.

From these results we can deduce the position of the centre of gravity of a heavy rectangular object.

It is only correct to use the term *centre of gravity* if an object is influenced by gravity, that is, if it has weight. If the rectangle considered here is a real object it must have a centre of gravity. This is the reason why it was described as being heavy. If its weight is not involved, the object is said to be *light* and to have a *centroid* at the position where the centre of gravity would be, had there been one. The term *centroid* is therefore only used for thin laminae. Notice that the words *thin* and *light* imply the absence of weight.

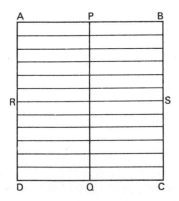

Figure 36. A rectangle considered as a series of narrow sections.

A rectangle can be considered as a series of narrow sections. Each of these may be a rectangle, as shown in fig. 36. The centroid (or the centre of gravity if the object has weight) of each of these is at its midpoint, so that the centroid of the rectangle ABCD in the figure can be found by finding the centroid of each of the small sections indicated by the horizontal lines. In every case, the centroids of the sections lie on the line PQ, where P and Q are the midpoints of AB and CD respectively. Thus the centroid of the rectangle must also lie on the line PQ.

Similarly, the rectangle can be divided vertically into sections. Again the centroid of each section lies on the line joining the midpoints of the sides, so the centroid of the rectangle lies on the line RS.

From this we can see that the centroid of the rectangle is at the point where the lines PQ and RS cross. It follows that for a solid figure, each of whose sides is a rectangle, the centre of gravity lies at a point midway between two opposite faces, on a line joining the centroids of the faces.

The argument which has been pursued here assumes that the density of the object is the same throughout, so that one part of it contributes as much weight as any other part of equal volume.

We can use this method to find the position of the centroid of an irregularly shaped lamina. We must first divide up the lamina into rectangles and then use the principle of moments to find the position of the centroid. Since the weight of a thin lamina is by definition zero, the areas are used in the calculations instead of their weights. It is then better to refer to the moments as *moments of area*. This method is illustrated in the following example.

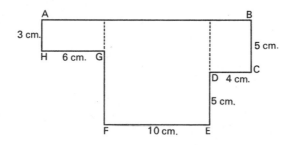

Figure 37. Diagram to show the division of a lamina into rectangles in order to find the position of its centroid.

The lamina shown in fig. 37 can be divided into three rectangles whose areas are 18 cm.², 100 cm.² and 20 cm.² The centroids of these rectangles are 3 cm., 11 cm. and 18 cm. from the line AH.

Then taking moments of area about AH

$$3 \times 18 + 11 \times 100 + 18 \times 20 = x \times 138$$

where the total area is 138 cm.² and x is the distance of the centroid of the whole figure from AH.

Thus $54 + 1100 + 360 = 138x$

or $x = \dfrac{1514}{138}$

so $x = 10\frac{67}{69}$ cm.

Then taking moments of area about the line, AB

$$1\tfrac{1}{2} \times 18 + 5 \times 100 + 2\tfrac{1}{2} \times 20 = y \times 138$$

where y is the distance of the centroid of the whole figure from AB.

Thus $27 + 500 + 50 = 138y$

or $y = \dfrac{577}{138}$

so $y = 4\frac{25}{138}$ cm.

From these results two lines can be drawn, one $10\frac{67}{69}$ cm. from AH and the other $4\frac{25}{138}$ cm. from AB. The centroid is at the point where these lines cross. From the complexity of the arithmetic, you will appreciate that it might be worthwhile to look for some way of reducing the work in finding the centroid.

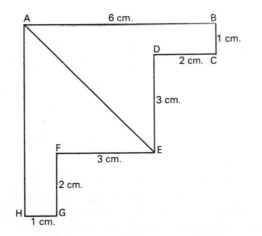

Figure 38.   Lamina which is symmetrical about AE.

Fig. 38 shows a lamina which can be seen to be symmetrical about the line AE. One should always be prepared to look for a line of symmetry, because the clockwise and anticlockwise moments about this line are equal and the centroid must therefore lie on it. A single calculation will now locate the centroid. If two or more lines of symmetry exist then the centroid will be at their intersection.

Problems 7.3

1. Find the distance of the centroid from the line AH in fig. 38.
2. A circular disc has a small concentric circular disc removed from it. Where is the centroid of the remaining ring? (This kind of figure is sometimes called an annulus.)
3. Draw a circular disc, radius 8 cm., on a piece of squared paper. By dividing half of it into a number of parallel strips and determining the area of each by counting squares on the paper, find the centroid of the semicircle.
4. Draw any triangle and by dividing it into a number of strips find a line on which the centroid must lie. Hence find the position of the centroid.
5. Fig. 39 shows a rectangular lamina, ABCD, in which a small rectangular hole, PQRS, has been cut. Find the position of the centroid of the remaining sheet.

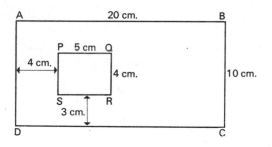

Figure 39.

NOTE: This question can be solved by dividing the figure into four rectangles. A quicker method is to subtract the moment of area of the hole. Then the moment of area of the rectangle ABCD less the moment of area of the hole PQRS is put equal to the moment of area of the figure (i.e. the area of the figure times the distance of the centroid from some given line).

Chapter 8
Circles and centroids

In this chapter we shall obtain more practice with some of the mathematical methods we have met previously and also extend these techniques.

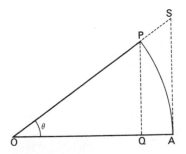

Figure 40. Diagram for comparing sin θ and tan θ.

The line OA in fig. 40 has been rotated through the angle θ so that it then takes up the position OP. We already know that tan θ = PQ/OQ and sin θ = PQ/OP. But OP = OA, and OA is clearly longer than OQ. From this information can you deduce whether sin θ is greater or less than tan θ? Is your result true for all angles between 0° and 90°?

Draw OA, about 25 cm. long, on a piece of paper, and with O as centre draw the arc of a circle through A. Hence for a number of angles θ, up to about 20°, measure the lengths of OQ, PQ and the distance round the arc AP, and record the results in a table similar to that shown here.

Table 14

OA = 25 cm.

θ	PQ	OQ	AP	sin θ = PQ/OP	tan θ = PQ/OQ	AP/OA
2°						
4°						
6°						
8°						

From the table which you have constructed you will see that for small angles the ratios PQ/OP, PQ/OQ, and AP/OA are all very nearly the same. As the angle becomes larger it becomes clear that the tangent is the largest of these ratios and the sine is the smallest. This is because OQ is less than OA, so that PQ/OQ is greater than PQ/OP. Also AP is always greater than PQ, so that AP/OA is always greater than PQ/OP.

An angle can be defined as the amount of the divergence between two lines. Two divergent lines can always be extended to meet in a point, as in fig. 40. If this point is the centre of the circle of which AP is an arc, the divergence can be expressed as the ratio of the length of the arc AP between the two divergent lines and the distance from the arc to their intersection. So we measure θ as AP/OA, although this ratio is clearly much less than unity in the example here and this method of calculation does not therefore give the result in degrees but instead measures angles in *radians*. For the angle to be 1 radian, AP must be equal to OA. If you measure this angle you will find that it is about 57° so that there are just over 3 radians in an angle of 180°. More accurately there are 2π radians in 360° ($\pi = 3.14159$ approx.).

Areas of figures

If OP be extended to S in fig. 40 and SA be drawn perpendicular to OA, it can be seen that the area of the segment OPA is greater than the area of the triangle OPQ and less than OSA. Before finding the area of the segment we must first examine the area of some triangles.

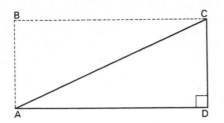

Figure 41. A right-angled triangle.

From fig. 41 it can be seen that the area of the triangle ACD is half that of the rectangle ABCD. The area is best remembered as 'one half of the length of the base times the perpendicular height'. This form of words is also appropriate for triangles which are not right angled.

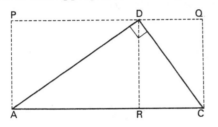

Figure 42. An acute-angled triangle.

For instance, in fig. 42 the area of the triangle ACD is $\frac{1}{2}$AC × DR. This can be seen by considering the triangle as composed of two triangles, ADR and CDR, the area of each of which is half that of a rectangle. These rectangles are APDR and DQCR. Thus the area of the whole triangle is one half of the area of the rectangle APQC.

If we examine figs. 41 and 42 closely we can see that the triangle ACD is really the same in each of them. What has changed has been our choice of which side to call the base, and therefore of which length is the perpendicular height. In fig. 41 the base is the side AD and in fig. 42 it is AC.

There are, however, other useful ways of writing down an expression for the area of a triangle. For example, in fig. 40 the area of the triangle OPQ is $\frac{1}{2}$PQ × OQ. But PQ = OQ tan θ.

Thus   area = $\frac{1}{2}$(OQ)^2 tan θ

Also   PQ = OP sin θ

Therefore   area = $\frac{1}{2}$OP.OQ sin θ

Again, the area of the triangle OSA

$$= \tfrac{1}{2}OS.SA$$

$$= \tfrac{1}{2}(OA)^2 \tan \theta$$

$$= \tfrac{1}{2}OS.OA \sin \theta$$

Now $\qquad \theta = AP/OA$

and if $\qquad OA = r$, the radius of the circle of which AP is an arc

$$AP = r\theta$$

This statement is always true, so long as θ is measured in radians.

When θ is small, the area of the segment is very nearly equal to $\tfrac{1}{2}OA \times PQ$, and (approximately) $PQ = AP$.

Therefore, area of segment $= \tfrac{1}{2}r^2\theta$.

Provided that θ is measured in radians this is true for all angles: the area of a circle for instance ($\theta = 2\pi$) is $\tfrac{1}{2}r^2 \times 2\pi = \pi r^2$, or if d is the diameter of the circle, its area is $\dfrac{\pi d^2}{4}$.

Problems 8.1

1. The circumference of a circle is 2π times its radius. How many radians are there in $90°$? How many degrees are there in 1 radian?

2. What is the area of the segment of a circle, radius 10 cm., whose angle is $10°$?

3. A right-angled triangle has a base 15 cm. long and a perpendicular side 10 cm. long. Find the angle of a segment of a circle whose radius is the base of the triangle, so that the areas of the two figures are equal.

4.

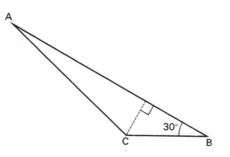

Figure 43.

In fig. 43, AB is 20 cm., CB is 5 cm., and the angle at B is 30°. Find the area of the triangle ABC.

5. In fig. 40 join A and P. If OA is 50 cm. and θ is 45° find the area of the sector of the circle cut off between the line AP and the arc AP.

Centroid of a triangle

The techniques for finding the centroids of figures (such as fig. 37) can be extended if the position of the centroid of a triangle is known. This was found (in problem 7.3.4) to be at the intersection of the lines from each of the angles to the midpoints of the opposite sides.

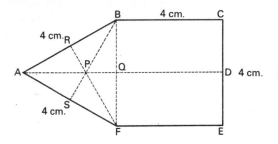

Figure 44.   Centroid of a lamina.

The centroid of the lamina shown in fig. 44 must clearly be on the line of symmetry, AD. Its distance from D can be found by taking moments of area about the line CE.

First consider the triangle ABF. Its centroid is at P, and the triangle is equilateral, so that the angle PFQ is 30°.

Thus $PQ = 2 \tan 30°$

$$= \frac{2\sqrt{3}}{3}$$

$$= 1{\cdot}15$$

The area of the triangle ABF $= 4 \tan 60°$

$$= 2\sqrt{3}$$

Thus, taking moments of area about the line CE

$$16 \times 2 + 2\sqrt{3} \times 5{\cdot}15 = x\,(16 + 2\sqrt{3}),$$

where x is the distance of the centroid from the line CE

$$32 + 17{\cdot}84 = 19{\cdot}46x$$

$$x = \frac{49{\cdot}84}{19{\cdot}46}$$

$$= 2{\cdot}56 \text{ cm.}$$

This problem is interesting because it shows that in the triangle ABF, $PQ = \dfrac{2\sqrt{3}}{3}$ and $AQ = 2\sqrt{3}$, so that P divides AQ, with $PQ = \dfrac{1}{3} AQ$.

It should be noticed that this was a particularly simple case since AQ met BF perpendicularly. The result of this was that AQ bisected the angle at A. It should not be thought that P is the point of intersection of the bisectors of the angles of the triangles in every case. P is the point of intersection of the lines from A, B and F to the midpoints of the opposite sides. This is so for all triangles.

Graphical method for a centroid

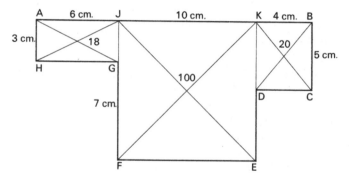

Figure 45. Centroid of a lamina (graphical method).

A method has already been described for calculating the position of the centroid of fig. 45 (see also fig. 37). A graphical method will now be considered. The figure also shows the area of each of the rectangles and the positions of their centroids. The figure should be drawn carefully, either full size or to a convenient scale, and then a graphical construction can be made to find the position of the centroid. This construction really depends on the principle of moments of area.

First letter the spaces P, Q, R and S between the lines of action of the centroids of the rectangles.

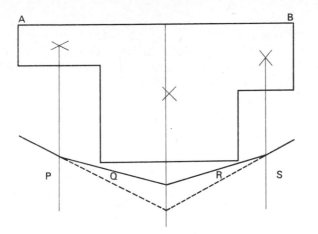

Figure 46. Centroid of a lamina : space diagram.

Fig. 47 shows a vertical line on which the points p, q, r and s correspond to these lines of action. The distances between them are proportional to the areas of the appropriate rectangles.

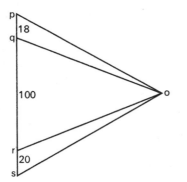

Figure 47. Construction for centroid of a lamina.

The point o is any convenient point, which is joined to each of the points p, q, r and s. These lines are then transferred end to end between the lines of action at the centroids, as shown in fig. 46. The continuations of the first and last of these lines intersect on the line of action at the centroid of the whole lamina. This line can then be placed on the figure.

A similar construction, but with fig. 46 rotated through a right-angle, will give a second line of action. The intersection of these lines will be at the centroid of the lamina. Alternatively, if there is a line of symmetry, only one line of action need be found, since the centroid must also lie on the line of symmetry.

A further example of this method is shown in fig. 48.

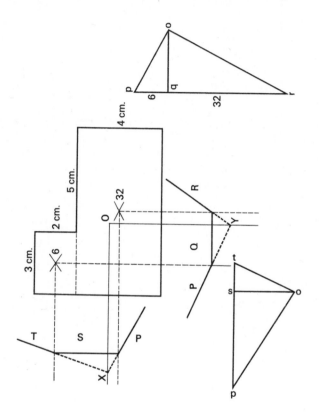

Figure 48.   Centroid of a lamina (graphical method).

The lamina was first seen to consist of two rectangles, whose areas are 6 cm.² and 32 cm.² Vertical lines of action were drawn so that the regions P, Q and R are produced. A space diagram is then drawn with points p, q and r and the pole, o, at a convenient point. The lines op, oq, and or are then transferred back parallel to the lines of the space diagram, and extended to meet at Y.

In the same way the regions P, S and T were used to construct a space diagram. The lines of the diagram, *op*, *os* and *ot*, enabled the point X to be found. The lines OX and OY intersect at O, the centroid of the lamina.

This method can only be used to obtain the position of the centroid with an accuracy which depends on the overall accuracy of the diagram. It may thus lack the precision of other mathematical methods. It also tends to be a lengthy procedure, although it does not increase much in complexity as the number of subdivisions of the lamina is increased. The chief advantage of the method is that it avoids some tedious mathematics, particularly where the subdivision involves triangular sections.

Experimental method for irregular laminae

The methods which have been described so far become difficult to apply if the shape of the lamina is irregular. The position of the centre of gravity of a metal sheet can be found experimentally by suspending it in turn from a number of points on its perimeter. This is illustrated in fig. 49.

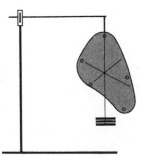

Figure 49. Apparatus to find the centroid of an irregularly shaped lamina.

The method depends on the sheet being freely suspended so that it will come to rest with its centre of gravity vertically below its point of suspension. A plumb line from the point of suspension can be used to show the line on which the centre of gravity must lie. When the plumb line and the sheet are at rest, the line can be lightly held against the sheet so that its direction can be marked. The experiment may be repeated a number of times, and it will be found that the lines of action all pass through the centroid of the sheet.

Problems 8.2

1. A right-angled triangle has two perpendicular sides 6 cm. and 8 cm. long. How far from the longer of these sides will the centroid of the triangle be?

2. A cone of metal is machined so that its height is 6 cm. and its right circular base has a radius of 8 cm. What is the position of the centroid of the cone?

3. Three uniform rods form the sides of a right-angled triangle, the rods forming the mutually perpendicular sides being 6 cm. and 8 cm. long. If the rods weigh 10 gf. per cm. length, find the weight of the structure and the position of its centroid.

4. The lamina shown in fig. 44 is constructed by joining a triangular steel sheet to a square steel sheet whose thickness is one half of that of the first sheet. (*a*) Find the position of the centre of gravity of the combined sheet. (*b*) What must the ratio of the thicknesses of the sheets be to make the centre of gravity fall on the line BF in the figure?

5. A uniform hollow metal cylinder has a right circular section, is 20 cm. long, and weighs 2 kgf. A uniform circular metal plate 2 cm. thick and weighing 500 gf. is fixed so that it covers one end of the cylinder. Find the position of the centre of gravity of (i) the cylinder, (ii) the plate, and (iii) the combined cylinder and plate.

Conclusion

In this book we have ranged over many topics, from atoms and molecules to errors of measurement and centres of gravity. If this has seemed to you no more than a collection of odds and ends of information, you should remember that a technician must be acquainted with a wide range of skills.

Here you have met an introduction to the mathematical tools you will need and an attempt has been made to help you to think in the logical way which makes mathematics easier to understand.

You will also have read something of scientific method, and perhaps you will have appreciated that all true science depends vitally on experiment. The worth of an experiment can only be judged if we first assess the errors to which it is liable and attempt to minimize them.

Much of the work which we have done has been related to the concept of energy. The idea of energy is fundamental since in the vast majority of circumstances energy is neither created nor destroyed. Thus we are able to consider energy as being conserved, and the study of heat, electricity, and mechanical motion all become studies of energy transfer.

Now you have come so far, you will want to perform new experiments and to examine new ideas. This must wait for a further book. However, before attempting to conquer new fields it is wise to consolidate the ground you have won. This book therefore concludes with some revision problems. If some of these cause difficulty you will know which parts of this book you need to read again.

Revision problems

1. A voltmeter is used to measure the potential drop across a resistor which is one of a chain of resistors across a direct voltage supply. Name at least three errors of measurement which might occur. Which of these can be minimized by taking successive readings to obtain an average? Which of them are systematic errors?

2. A rectangular piece of metal has sides 12.96 ± 0.04 cm. and 7.81 ± 0.04 cm. Find the area of the sheet.

3. The volume of a cylinder with a length l and a circular end face radius r is $\pi r^2 l$. If r is measured as 10.0 ± 0.08 cm. and l as 25.0 ± 0.05 cm., find the volume of the cylinder. Assume π is known with negligible error.

4. Ten students each record the atmospheric pressure as part of an experiment. State the most likely average value of the pressure and the accuracy with which it can be given. The readings were taken in order, at equal intervals of time, over a period of 15 minutes. Is there any evidence that pressure was rising or falling during this time?

i.	75·98 cm.	vi.	75·96 cm.
ii.	75·97 cm.	vii.	75·97 cm.
iii.	76·00 cm.	viii.	75·96 cm.
iv.	75·97 cm.	ix.	75·98 cm.
v.	75·97 cm.	x.	75·96 cm.

5. The following results show the time, T, taken for one complete oscillation of a simple pendulum. Plot these results as a graph of $T = k\sqrt{l}$ where l is the length of the pendulum. Hence find the probable value of the constant, k, and assess the accuracy with which it can be stated. What can you deduce if, from other information, it is known that the correct value for k is $42.40 \pm 0.10 \times 10^{-3}$?

T	l
seconds	cm.
1·55	60
1·80	80
2·01	100
2·20	120
2·37	140
2·54	160
2·69	180

6. Distinguish between mass and weight. In what units may they be measured?

7. If 1 cu. ft of sea water weighs 64 lbf., find the weight in tons of a cubic mile of sea water.

8. If 1 cu. ft of sea water weighs 64 lbf., find the density of sea water in g.cm.$^{-3}$

9. A metal object has a volume of 5 cm.^{3} and a density of 8·45 g.cm.$^{-3}$ Find its mass.

10. If the density of petrol is 46·78 lb. ft.$^{-3}$, find its density in M.K.S. units (kg.m.$^{-3}$).

11. What is an element? From table 4 find the molecular weight of chloroform ($CHCl_3$).

12. Distinguish between physical and chemical changes, and give an example of each.

13. A compound contains approximately 27 per cent of carbon and 73 per cent oxygen. Find its chemical formula.

14. Potassium chlorate ($KClO_3$) is often used as a source of oxygen. What percentage of oxygen is present in it?

15. If the atomic weight of sodium is 23 and its atomic number is 11, what is its atomic structure?

16. Which requires the more heat energy, heating 20 g. of sand through 30 centigrade degrees, or heating 5 g. of olive oil through 49 centigrade degrees? Take the specific heat of sand as 0·19 and olive oil as 0·47.

17. A 20 g. piece of copper (specific heat 0·1 cal.g.$^{-1}$ deg.$^{-1}$C.) is heated in a flame to 350°C., plunged into 150 g. of water at 25°C., and stirred well. What is the maximum temperature subsequently reached by the water?

18. A cooling system immersed in 40 kg. of water at 4°C. extracts 30,000 calories per minute. If the latent heat of ice is 80 cal.g.$^{-1}$ how long will it take before all the water is frozen?

19. A piece of metal whose mass is 220 g. and specific heat is 0·09 cal. g.$^{-1}$ deg.$^{-1}$C. is suspended in steam above freely boiling water. It is quickly transferred to a piece of ice at 0°C. Find the mass of ice melted.

20. What is understood by the mechanical equivalent of heat? Lead shot weighing 250 g. is quickly inverted 800 times, each time falling through a height of 1 metre in a cardboard tube. Find the total work done in joules. If 46·8 calories of heat are produced, find (i) the temperature rise in the lead, and (ii) the mechanical equivalent of heat (specific heat of lead is 0·03 cal. g.$^{-1}$ deg.$^{-1}$C.).

21. (a) What do you understand by the effects of an electric current? List them, giving an example of each.

(b) How long will it take to pass an electric charge of 1000 coulombs by a 12 volt battery which is connected to a 72 ohm load?

22. What is understood by the electrochemical equivalent of a metal? The resistance of a silver plating bath is 2 ohms. If it is operated from a 10 volt source, find how long it will take to plate 100 g. of silver in the bath (the electrochemical equivalent of silver is 1·18 milligrams/coulomb.

23. A uniform copper wire is 10 metres long and its cross-sectional area is 1 mm.^{2} Find (i) the resistance of the wire, and (ii) the length of iron wire of the same cross-sectional area which has the same resistance as the copper wire (table 8 gives the resistivities of these metals).

24. A 100 watt electric blanket is operated continuously for 1 hour. How many calories of heat are produced?

25. Three resistors, each of 500 ohms resistance, form the sides of a triangle. What is the effective resistance between the ends of any side of the triangle?

26. A current meter reads 100 microamperes full scale. If its resistance is 20 ohms, find the voltage which is developed across it at full-scale deflection. Hence find what resistance should be placed in series with it if the combination is to read 1 volt full-scale.

27. A stake is fixed vertically in the ground and has two ropes tied to it so that they may be pulled horizontally. The first is pulled with a force of 100 lbf., and the second, at right angles to it, with a force of 50 lbf. What resultant force is acting on the stake?

28. A weight of 1 kgf. is suspended from a point by a cord 1 metre long. The weight is also tied to a cord which is pulled horizontally so that the weight is deflected and hangs 500 cm. to one side of its original position. Find the force in the horizontal cord.

29. A uniform plank 4 metres long weighs 20 kgf. and rests with 3 metres of its length on a flat surface over the end of which the plank protrudes. A man weighing 60 kgf. walks along the plank. Find how far he is from

the end when it topples. Find also the least weight which must be placed on the end of the plank if the man is to be able to reach the other end.

30. A man weighing 64 kgf. stands on a 4 metre plank which is placed symmetrically on two trestles 2 metres apart. Find where the man must stand if one of the reactions at the trestles is twice that at the other one. The weight of the plank is 16 kgf.

31. Three rods of equal length, l, are joined to form the sides of an equilateral triangle, ABC. The rod which forms the side AB is twice as heavy as either of the others. Find the position of the centre of gravity of the structure.

32. A pendulum consists of a uniform circular disc 10 cm. in diameter and weighing 650 gf. together with a uniform rod 1 metre long weighing 400 gf. which is fixed normally to a point on the circumference of the disc. If the pendulum rocks about a point 2 cm. from the end of the rod, find the distance from the pivot to the centre of gravity of the rod.

33. In fig. 50 the length of the side c is given by

$$c^2 = a^2 + b^2 - 2ab \cos C.$$

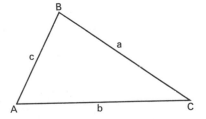

Figure 50.

Use this to calculate the angles of a triangle, whose sides are 3 cm., 4 cm. and 5 cm.

34. A triangle has angles 50°, 50° and 80°. If the longest side is 10 cm. long, find the lengths of the other sides.

35. A force of 10 kgf. acts at an angle of 30° to the horizontal and a second force, also of 10 kgf., acts at the same point at an angle of 70° to the first force and 80° to the horizontal. Find the horizontal and vertical components of these forces, and hence find their resultant and the angle at which it acts.

36. A maltese cross consists of four equilateral triangles which meet at a point so that the angles between them are equal. If the sides of each of the triangles are of length $2l$, and one of the triangles is then removed, find the position of the centroid of the remaining figure.

37. An object weighing 1 kgf. rests on a rough inclined plane. If it is on the point of slipping down the plane when the angle of inclination to the horizontal is 20°, find the frictional force and the reaction normal to the plane.

38. (a) Write down the following angles in radian units: 30°, 45°, 60°.

(b) Find the area of an equilateral triangle of side $2l$, from which the largest possible circular piece has been removed.

39. Describe in detail the nature of the air, commenting on its composition and the effects of water vapour, industrial smoke, and dust when these are present.

40. Outline the differences in atomic structure which enable us to distinguish between elements. What bearing has this on the conduction of electricity?

Appendix

This appendix deals with some of the introductory aspects of engineering science and mathematics: a knowledge of the material in it is assumed in the remainder of the book. Certain additional data, which is not necessary to the understanding of the rest of this volume, has also been included for easy reference; this is indicated by an asterisk (*).

Common factors

$$10 = 5 \times 2 \times 1$$

5, 2 and 1 are said to be factors of 10. Similarly 6, 2 and 1 are factors of 12. Also, the factors of 6 are 3, 2 and 1 so that we may say that the factors of 12 are 3, 2, 2 and 1. The factors of a number, when multiplied together, give that number.

Thus $\quad 3 \times 2 \times 2 \times 1 = 12$

When one number is divided by another, the division can be simplified if one can quickly recognize the presence of factors which are common to both numbers. For example, $\frac{42}{12}$ can be written as

$$\frac{7.3.2.1}{3.2.2.1}$$

and by cancelling common factors this reduces to $\frac{7}{2}$ or 3·5.

The same principle applies to the removal of factors which are algebraic. Thus, $\frac{8x^3}{7x}$ becomes $\frac{8}{7}x^2$ and

$$\frac{7(x+1)}{(x+1)^2} = \frac{7}{x+1}$$

It is not always easy to recognize a common factor: the last example could have been written as

$$\frac{7x+7}{x^2+2x+1}$$

so that the common factor, $x+1$, would not have been so obvious.

Algebraic factors can often only be discovered by careful inspection. Where an expression contains a quadratic, such as $x^2 + 2x + 1$ in the previous example, it is frequently worth while finding the roots of the quadratic in case one should be a common factor.

Thus $\quad y = \dfrac{x+1}{x^2-1}$

can be simplified since $x^2 - 1 = (x+1)(x-1)$ so that $y = \dfrac{1}{(x-1)}$.

Elementary textbooks in pure mathematics give examples of the techniques for solving quadratic equations.

Numerical common factors are not necessarily integers (whole numbers). Thus $\frac{1 \cdot 2}{0 \cdot 3}$ may be regarded as having a common factor of 0·3, so that it simplifies to 4. You may prefer first to multiply both the denominator and the numerator of the fraction by some convenient number. Here, if the fraction is multiplied by 10 in this way, it becomes $\frac{12}{3}$, so that the result, 4, becomes more obvious.

It is always possible to treat a fraction in this way, provided that the numerator and the denominator are treated alike, and that we are careful that the *whole* of the numerator and the *whole* of the denominator are dealt with.

Thus $\quad \dfrac{1 \cdot 2}{0 \cdot 3 + 6 \cdot 0}$

cannot be simplified unless both the terms in the denominator are multiplied. Alternatively, in this case, these terms can be added before multiplication to give $\frac{1 \cdot 2}{6 \cdot 3}$, so that $\frac{12}{63}$ can be simplified to $\frac{4}{21}$.

Aids to calculation

In this book there are many calculations to be carried out when reading the text, and in the problems associated with each chapter. One reason for this is to give the reader so much practice that by the time he has reached the end of the book simple calculations are second nature to him. However, if these calculations are carried out by traditional arithmetic with paper and pencil they will be very tedious, and for this reason the reader is advised to use some aids to calculation. The use of tables of logarithms, squares, square roots and so forth are recommended, but if one is not careful tables of logarithms come to be regarded as the only mathematical aid which is available and a misapprehension arises that four-figure logarithm tables are precise. This is far from the truth, for they are frequently only approximations.

In many colleges use is made of mechanical and electric desk calculators which give answers correct to ten or more places, and these machines are even becoming available in some schools. There are occasions when such accuracy is important (for instance when examining the difference between very similar quantities) so the reader should if possible obtain practice at using calculators of this type.

The slide rule

For many everyday purposes the slide rule is a useful aid to calculation. The accuracy with which results can be obtained largely depends on the care with which it is used, but even a cheap slide rule should give results correct to three significant figures.

It is also important to remember that errors can often be avoided by rough checks of the order of the expected result, so that the placing of the decimal point can be carried out correctly. The slide rule does not itself give the position of the decimal point: this must be decided by inspection so that the use of a slide rule will act as a constant reminder to carry out rough checks.

It is not proposed to describe in detail the operation of a slide rule, since when a rule is purchased the manufacturer usually gives a booklet of precise instructions with it. A few general points, however, are worth noting.

The rule consists of a stock and a movable slide which is held between the sides of the stock. There is also a cursor (a fine line engraved on a piece of plastic) which can be moved to any part of the stock. The slide and the stock carry logarithmic scales (see chapter 1). One reason for this is to carry out multiplication and division, but an added reason is that this type of scale gives a uniform proportional accuracy, so that the three significant figures referred to previously are maintained for all parts of the scale.

Since the scales are logarithmic, multiplication is carried out by adding the logarithmic lengths which correspond to the numbers, and division by subtracting them. These scales run in the same direction along the slide and the stock.

Often there is an additional scale on the slide which runs in the opposite direction. This is the reciprocal scale. It can be used to obtain reciprocals by comparison with the first scale on the slide and for certain other calculations, such as more rapid multiplication and division. All this, and the use of other scales, will be described in the manufacturer's booklet.

Plane figures

For the purposes of revision, the formulae for calculating the areas and perimeters of a number of plane figures are given here. These formulae may be deduced in a number of ways. For example, if a rectangle of sides a and b be drawn on squared paper so that one side corresponds to a squares and the other to b squares, then the number of squares enclosed by the rectangle will correspond to ab squares. Therefore, we say that the area of a rectangle with sides a and b is equal to $a \times b$.

It should be noticed that the area of a trapezium depends only on the average length of the parallel sides and the perpendicular distance (p) between them. If one of these sides has zero length, then the formula becomes $\frac{1}{2} ap$, which is the formula for the area of a triangle.

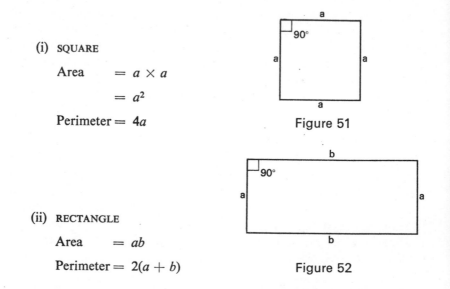

(i) SQUARE

Area $= a \times a$

$= a^2$

Perimeter $= 4a$

Figure 51

(ii) RECTANGLE

Area $= ab$

Perimeter $= 2(a + b)$

Figure 52

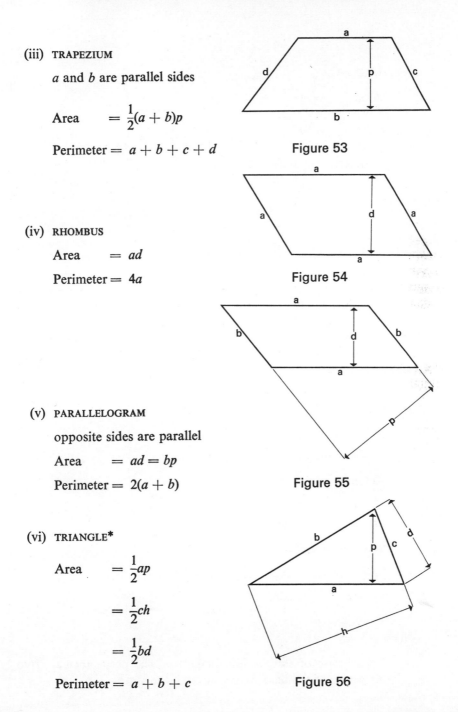

(iii) TRAPEZIUM

    a and *b* are parallel sides

    Area $= \frac{1}{2}(a + b)p$

    Perimeter $= a + b + c + d$

Figure 53

(iv) RHOMBUS

    Area $= ad$

    Perimeter $= 4a$

Figure 54

(v) PARALLELOGRAM

    opposite sides are parallel

    Area $= ad = bp$

    Perimeter $= 2(a + b)$

Figure 55

(vi) TRIANGLE*

    Area $= \frac{1}{2}ap$

              $= \frac{1}{2}ch$

              $= \frac{1}{2}bd$

    Perimeter $= a + b + c$

Figure 56

(vii) CIRCLE*

Area $= \pi r^2$

$= \pi \dfrac{d^2}{4}$

Perimeter (circumference)

$= 2\pi r$

$= \pi d$

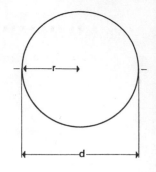

Figure 57

Surface areas and volumes of some common solids

A similar method to that used for the area of plane figures can be used for solid figures. Thus, if a rectangular solid be constructed of cubes, each of side 1 cm., so that its sides are a cm., b cm. and c cm., then the solid will contain abc cubes. If the solid is itself a cube of side a cm., then the volume will be $a \times a \times a$ cm.^{3}, that is a^3 cm.^{3} The surface area of each side of the cube will be a^2 cm.^{2} so that the total surface area of all the six sides will be $6a^2$.

(i) CUBE

Side $= a$

Surface area $= 6a^2$

Volume $= a^3$

(ii) RECTANGULAR SOLID

Sides $= a, b, c$

Surface area $= 2(ab + bc + ac)$

Volume $= abc$

(iii) PYRAMID*

Square base of side, a, and height, h. The perpendicular from the centre of the base passes through the vertex.

Surface area $= a^2 + 2a\sqrt{\left(h^2 + \dfrac{a^2}{4}\right)}$

Volume $= \dfrac{1}{3}\,a^2h$

(iv) CONE*

Circular base of radius, r, and height, h. The perpendicular from the centre of the base passes through the vertex.

Surface area $= \pi r^2 + \pi r\sqrt{(h^2 + r^2)}$

Volume $= \dfrac{1}{3}\,\pi r^2 h$

(v) SPHERE*

Radius $= r$

Surface area $= 4\pi r^2$

Volume $= \dfrac{4}{3}\,\pi r^3$

Solutions to problems

1.1   The incorrect results are nos. 1, 5, 8, 10.

1.2   1   24·00   3   42·86   5   32·25
      2   42·00   4   54·60

1.3   1   (*a*) 14·41 max. percentage error −12·98
          (*b*) 15·12   −17·06
          (*c*) 15·00   +16·93
      2   (*a*) 45 per cent   (*b*) 70 per cent

1.4   1   (*a*) 100,000:1   3   50
          (*b*) 10^{10}:1   4   21·6 cm.
      2   2·4 × 3·6 m.   5   just over 5 hours 56 minutes

1.5   1   18·52   5   1·382   9   3·247
      2   274·6   6   3·659   10   13·93
      3   1·602   7   7·242
      4   2·283   8   1·042

1.6   1   (*a*) 0·04877; (*b*) correct; (*c*) correct; (*d*) 19·19; (*e*) $\overline{2}$·2695
      2   24·60;   1·685;   1·020;   0·9899;
           0·04065; 0·5934; 0·9804; 1·010
      3   17·6 — 26·4
          21·6 — 32·4
          26·4 — 39·6
          31·2 — 46·8
          37·6 — 56·4
          eliminate 27 and 39

4 2·629 (enough)
  81·41 (not enough)
  9·303 (enough)

2.1 1 39·37 in. (note, however, that to be more accurate there are
        39·370147 inches in 1 metre).
    2 6·45 sq. mm.   4 18·1   6 25·400 mm.
    3 39·373 in.   5 29·92 in.

2.2 1 weights
    2 1417·5 g., $\frac{1}{1\cdot4175}$ (= 0·71) litres

2.3 1 (a) 33·97 × 10^6 cm.sec.; (b) 33·97 × 10^4 m.sec. (c) 1115 f.p.s.
    2 (a) 0·9971 g.cm.^{3}; (b) 997·1 kg.m.^{3}
    3 0·18 cm.^{3} 4 0·87153 cm.^{2} 5 63·68 lb.

2.4 3 1033·6 g.
    4 9·88 g.
    5 8300 kg.m.$^{-3}$

3.1 1 $C + O_2 = CO_2$; 44·01
    2 $2Na + 2H_2O = H_2 + 2NaOH$
      39·998
    3 approximately 27 g.
    4 249·68; 143·34

3.2 2 not more than 17·4 g. iron for every 10 g. sulphur
    3 about 25·4 per cent   4 CH_4 5 35 per cent

3.3 6 9 protons, 10 neutrons, 9 electrons   7 10   8 2, 28·9

4.2 1 sea water
    3 148·1 calories; just over 1·85 g.
    4 ammonia: 145·5 calories
      sulphur dioxide: 98 calories
    5 356°C.
    6 average is 362·8°C., so likely value is 360°C. + 50°C. or −35°C.

4.3 3 80 cal. g.$^{-1}$ 5 95·4°C.
    4 500 cal. lost to surroundings

4.4 1 0·23 deg.C.   3 21168 joules; losses to the air
    2 265 deg.C.   4 28 watts
                             5 170 seconds

4.5　1　nickel steel
　　2　iron
　　3　less than 24×10^{-6} deg.$^{-1}$C. (actually 21)
　　4　62·9 cm.
　　5　copper 72·6 cm., iron 27·4 cm.

5.1　1　just under $6\frac{1}{2}$ minutes　　3　41·6 A.m.$^{-2}$　　4　156 minutes

5.2　1　$I = \dfrac{Val}{\rho}$
　　2　8 A.; 31·25 ohms
　　4　18,000
　　5　(i) $\frac{1}{4}$ volt; (ii) $\frac{3}{4}$ volt; (iii) 2 volts.
　　6　AB $= 40$ cm.; 8 ohms, 92 ohms; 5 volts.

5.3　1　0·004 deg.$^{-1}$C.; 40·6 ohms
　　2　600 ohms
　　3　4 ohms; $\frac{1}{4}$ watt for each parallel resistor and $\frac{1}{2}$ watt for the series resistor
　　4　100 mA. for each series circuit of 10 lamps
　　5　0·1 volt (100 mV.), 11 A.
　　6　2·78 ohms
　　7　pressure, temperature
　　8　4 A., 10 A.

6.1　1　$10 \sqrt{41}$ kgf. at 128° 40′ with the direction in which A pulls, or 141° 21′ with the direction in which B pulls
　　2　73·9 kgf.　　　　　　4　707 gf.
　　3　54·55 gf.　　　　　　5　R $=$ T $= 707$ gf.

6.2　1　$R_1 = 409, 353, 298, 270$ g.
　　　　$R_2 = 131, 187, 242, 270$ g.
　　2　$R_1 = 764·5$ g., $R_2 = 175·5$ g. approx.
　　3　1·25 kgf.; less force is needed
　　4　1·78 kgf. Note: it is only possible to satisfy the conditions of this question when the side of 50 cm. is horizontal.
　　5　2·54 kgf.

6.3　1　$0·2 \sqrt{97}$ kgf.; 23° 58′
　　2　Tension $= 2·065$ kgf., horizontal reaction $= 1·795$ kgf.
　　3　250 g., mechanical advantage $= 4$
　　　　25 g., mechanical advantage $= 40$
　　　　667 g.

4 Compression, AB $= 25 \sqrt{3}$ kgf.
Compression, AC $= 25$ kgf.
Tension   BC $= 12\cdot5 \sqrt{3}$ kgf.
Reaction at   B $= 37\cdot5$ kgf.
Reaction at   C $= 12\cdot5$ kgf.

5 Effort $= 714$ gf. Mechanical advantage $= 0\cdot28$
Note that the mechanical advantage is less than unity since the effort which is needed is greater than the load lifted.

7.1 2 $T = 1\cdot41$ kgf.   3 $T = 1\cdot25$ kgf.
$F = 0\cdot707$ kgf.   5 AD $= 15$ cm., CD $= 5 \sqrt{3}$ cm.

7.2 1

	0°	30°	45°	60°	90°
sine	0	$\frac{1}{2}$	$\sqrt{2}/2$	$\sqrt{3}/2$	1
cosine	1	$\sqrt{3}/2$	$\sqrt{2}/2$	$\frac{1}{2}$	0
tangent	0	$\sqrt{3}/3$	1	$\sqrt{3}$	∞

2 100 m.   4 (i) $\sqrt{3}$; (ii) 2 bars.
3 10 km., 1 km.   5 53° 8′; 4·53 m.

7.3 1 2·15 cm.
2 at the centre of the ring
3 on the line of symmetry 3 cm. from the centre
4 on the intersection of the lines from each angle to the midpoint of the opposite sides
5 5 cm. from AB, $10 \frac{7}{18}$ cm. from AD

8.1 1 $\frac{\pi}{2}$; 57·296°   4 25 cm.²
2 8·72 cm.²   5 approximately 99 cm.²
3 38° 12′

8.2 1 2 cm.
2 2 cm. above the base on the line of symmetry
3 240 gf.; at the same point as for a triangular lamina of the same size
4 (a) 2·95 cm. from CE on the line of symmetry; (b) 8:1
5 (i) on the axis 10 cm. from one end; (ii) 1 cm. from the centre of one face, in the metal; (iii) 12·2 cm. from the open end

Revision problems

2   $101 \cdot 2176 \pm 0 \cdot 0084$

3   $2500\pi \pm 0 \cdot 036\pi$

4   $75 \cdot 972 \pm 0 \cdot 0065$

5   $k = (40 \cdot 27 \pm 0 \cdot 11) \times 10^{-3}$ subject to systematic error

7   $4 \cdot 206 \times 10^9$ tons

8   $1 \cdot 02$ g. cm.$^{-3}$

9   $42 \cdot 25$ g.

10   754 kg.m.$^{-3}$

11   $119 \cdot 39$

13   CO_2

14   approx. 39 per cent

15   11 protons, 12 neutrons, 11 orbital electrons

16   sand requires 114 cal., olive oil requires $115 \cdot 1$ cal.

17   $29 \cdot 2°C.$

18   112 minutes

19   $247 \cdot 5$ g.

20   $196 \cdot 2$ joules; (i) $6 \cdot 2$ deg.C.; (ii) 42 cal.g.$^{-1}$

21   100 minutes

22   1695 seconds

23   $0 \cdot 16$ ohm; $1 \cdot 45$ metres

24   85,714 calories

25   333 ohms

26   2 mV., 9980 ohms

27   $50 \sqrt{5}$ lbf.

28   $333 \sqrt{3}$ gf.

29   $\frac{2}{3}$ metre from the end; $13\frac{1}{3}$ kgf.

30   $\frac{17}{12}$ metres from the end nearer the greater reaction

31   on the line of symmetry through C $\dfrac{3\sqrt{3}}{8}$ l from C towards AB

32   $\frac{821}{21}$ cm. from pivot

33   53° 8′; 36° 52′; 90° ′

34   $7 \cdot 78$ cm.

35   vertical $14 \cdot 85$, horizontal $6 \cdot 92$; resultant $16 \cdot 38$; angle 64° 57′ to horizontal

36   $\frac{2}{9}\sqrt{3}l$ from the point where the triangles are joined and on the line of symmetry

37   $F = 342$ gf., $R = 939 \cdot 7$ gf.

38   (a) $\dfrac{\pi}{6}, \dfrac{\pi}{4}, \dfrac{\pi}{3}$

      (b) $\dfrac{3\sqrt{3} - \pi}{3}$ l^2

Index

Penguin Library of Technology

General Editor: F. W. Kellaway
Principal, Letchworth College of Technology

This series will meet the needs of a wide range of students in technology, especially at the pre-university level. The first titles, for publication in autumn 1967, are:

Workshop processes and materials for engineering technicians, Vol. 1
by Dr J. A. Rankin, University of Aston in Birmingham

Fundamentals of engineering science and mathematics, Vol. 1
by K. J. Dean, Letchworth College of Technology

Telecommunication for technicians, Vol. 1
by D. Coatesworth, Principal, County Technical College, King's Lynn

In Preparation

Workshop processes and materials for engineering technicians, Vol. 2
by J. A. Rankin, University of Aston in Birmingham

A general course in engineering materials and workshop processes
by J. L. Gwyther and R. V. Page, Letchworth College of Technology

Ordinary national certificate mathematics, Vols. 1 and 2
by J. Dobinson, H.M. Dockyard Technical College, Chatham

Numerical methods
by K. J. Bowcock and M. J. Doubleday, University of Aston in Birmingham

Telecommunication for technicians, Vols. 2 and 3
by D. Coatesworth, Principal, County Technical College, King's Lynn

Fundamentals of engineering science and mathematics, Vols. 2 and 3
by K. J. Dean, Letchworth College of Technology

Workshop processes and materials for mechanical engineering technicians
Volume one

J. A. Rankin

Workshop Processes and Materials for Mechanical Engineering Technicians has been specially written around the first-year syllabus of the City and Guilds of London Institute Mechanical Engineering Technicians course (293), but will also provide a ready source of reference for a wide audience of students at Colleges of Further Education and Universities.

The author, Dr J. A. Rankin, has extensive experience of both engineering practice in industry and engineering research and development work. He now lectures on mechanics, materials and design at the University of Aston in Birmingham, where he has particular responsibility for organizing industrial training programmes on 'sandwich' degree courses.

Telecommunication for technicians
Volume one

D. Coatesworth

This book, the first in a series of volumes on telecommunication engineering for technicians, deals mainly with the electrical and electronic principles governing the behaviour of transistors, valves, and circuits. Particular importance has been attached to clarity of presentation so that this volume will be just as useful to the reader studying in his own home as to the student attending a college course (such as the City and Guilds of London Institute course for telecommunication technicians).

The author has nearly thirty years experience as a telecommunication engineer, including a wide variety of teaching posts from the technical level to university standard. A Fellow of the Institute of Electrical Engineers, he is now Principal of the County Technical College, King's Lynn.

Pelicans on science and technology

Why Smash Atoms
A. K. Soloman

First published in 1940, this famous Pelican describes the nature, purposes, and achievements of nuclear physics, stressing the contribution it has made to the basic understanding of nature. It was fully revised in 1959, and contains 32 pages of plates and numerous drawings in the text.

The Age of Automation
Sir Leon Bagrit

In these six Reith lectures Sir Leon Bagrit, the chairman of Elliott-Automation Ltd, clears up the current misconception about automation and explains how, unlike mechanization, it is chiefly a question of extending man's natural faculties by means of machines.

Boundaries of Science
Magnus Pyke

Beginning by discussing the growing interdependence of chemistry, physics, and biology, the author looks to the future, trying to answer the question: do scientists themselves place any definite limit on the possibilities of science? What, in fact, are the boundaries of science?

The Common Sense of Science
J. Bronowski

This book is an attempt to clear away some of the jargon that surrounds science, and to translate it into language that can be understood by an intelligent reader with no scientific knowledge.

The Science of Science
Ed Maurice Goldsmith & Alan Mackay

It was J. D. Bernal who first foreshadowed the need for a science of science on which a strategy for research could be based. Now, twenty-five years later, a group of leading scientists and writers assess how far its recommendations have been fulfilled and suggest what else needs to be done.

Crystals, Diamonds and Transistors
L. W. Marrison

A research chemist explains what crystals are and how they grow. From an analysis of the minor structure and faults of crystals the author then shows how science has exploited their properties to develop transistors, photography televisions, lasers and many other inventions.

Electronic Computors
S. H. Hollindale

Although little more than twenty years old, electronic computers are reshaping our technological society. This Pelican explains how computers work, how problems are presented to them and what sort of jobs they can tackle.

Mathematics in Management
Albert Battersby

Specially written for managers and others, to provide a sound basis of knowledge about the methods of operational research now being applied in public industries and services.

Penguin Technology Survey 1967
Ed Arthur Garratt

Presents new advances and trends in technology so that the intelligent man and woman may appreciate the magnitude of the technological revolution.

A Dictionary of Biology
M. Abercrombie, C. J. Hickman & M. L. Johnson

Explains the thousand or so terms which a layman may meet when reading scientific literature, and which a student of biology has to master at the beginning of his career.

A Dictionary of Electronics
S. Handel

A complete guide for both the student and the non-technical reader to the terms currently used in automation, radar, television, communications, navigation, and the manufacture and maintenance of computers and artificial satellites.

A Dictionary of Science
E. B. Uvarov, D. R. Chapman & Alan Isaacs

With over 4,000 entries this book covers the latest developments in atomic energy, astronomy, isotopes, mathematics, and physics.